First published 1955

SIR ISAAC PITMAN & SONS, LTD.
PITMAN HOUSE, PARKER STREET, KINGSWAY, LONDON, W.C.2
THE PITMAN PRESS, BATH
PITMAN HOUSE, LITTLE COLLINS STREET, MELBOURNE
27 BECKETTS BUILDINGS, PRESIDENT STREET, JOHANNESBURG

ASSOCIATED COMPANIES
PITMAN PUBLISHING CORPORATION
2 WEST 45TH STREET, NEW YORK

SIR ISAAC PITMAN & SONS (CANADA), LTD.
(INCORPORATING THE COMMERCIAL TEXT BOOK COMPANY)
PITMAN HOUSE, 381–383 CHURCH STREET, TORONTO

MADE IN GREAT BRITAIN AT THE PITMAN PRESS, BATH
E5—(T.763)

INSECTS and SPIDERS

A Book of Keys with Biological Notes

BY

C. P. FRIEDLANDER

B.Sc., A.R.C.S., F.R.E.S.

*Senior Biology Master at St. Benedict's School,
Former Member of the Staff of Whitgift School*

AND

D. A. PRIEST

B.Sc., A.R.C.S., F.Z.S.

*Biology Master at Peterborough County
Grammar School for Girls*

LONDON
SIR ISAAC PITMAN & SONS, LTD.

To My Mother—C. P. F.

To E. M. R.—D. A. P.

PREFACE

FEW would deny that one of the chief difficulties facing the biology teacher who seeks to give field-work its rightful place in middle and upper-school classes is that of identifying the material collected. Plants present perhaps the least difficulty, since floras and other works of reference are plentiful. Similar conditions apply to the identification of butterflies and moths, birds and the larger forms of pond life, but the huge number of species of the remaining insects and of spiders, coupled often with their small size, has caused them to be neglected and indeed almost overlooked at school level. Works of reference are often costly, inaccessible and deal with only a small part of the subject.

This book is an attempt to present the classification of insects and spiders in a simple yet scientific manner, and thus foster the inclusion of these groups in the standard field-work projects of schools. It should also be of use in the first year of a general biological degree course and to the layman who is prepared to take more trouble than is required to follow some of the more popular books on identification. Nearly all the features referred to can be seen with the aid of a hand lens magnifying eight times. The most important parts of the book are the keys to the families of insects and those to the families and genera of spiders, together with the biological notes. Comparatively few species of spiders have been described, and still fewer species of insects—a result to be expected in view of the numbers involved. In general the species described have been selected from amongst those most commonly found in the South of England—though some rarer examples have been included in order to illustrate the range of form. The keys serve only for adult specimens which exceed 3 mm in length. (Unless otherwise stated, dimensions refer to the length of the whole body *excluding* appendages.)

The authors are convinced that there is real value in identifying an insect as far as its family and a spider as far as its genus;

these divisions generally have ecological and economic significance. In the keys, features such as colour and size have been used where they are biologically significant (or for simplicity), but have been avoided elsewhere in favour of more fundamental features of structure. In this way it is hoped that teachers will be enabled to draw attention to the relationships between the various groups and the adaptations to mode of life. For those who wish to study further any particular group, a list of suitable books has been added at the end.

The value of any key is greatly increased by the assistance of a teacher, whether he be a specialist or not. However, it is believed that senior pupils should be able to use the book successfully alone, provided that the *alternatives* in the keys are read and *compared* very carefully, and that frequent reference is made to the figures. The figures are intended mainly to illustrate the general form of the families and features of structure, and consequently no scale of size has been given, though almost all the figures have been specially drawn from specimens in the authors' possession.

The naming of species has been brought up to date as far as possible. For insects the work used was *A Check List of British Insects* by G. S. Kloet and W. D. Hincks, 1945. The nomenclature of spiders was taken from *British Spiders* by G. H. Locket and A. F. Millidge (*see* book list) and from the synonymic index in *The Comity of Spiders* by W. S. Bristowe, 1939–41 (Vol. 2).

Thanks are due to C. T. Prime, M.A., Ph.D., F.L.S., Senior Biology Master at Whitgift School, for his interest and encouragement, and, not least, for his stimulating approach to the study of plants and animals in the field.

C. P. Friedlander has been responsible for the insect section and D. A. Priest for the other groups. The authors will welcome corrections of errors, and suggestions for improving the keys and the general usefulness of the book.

CONTENTS

ARTHROPODS

THE word "Arthropod" covers a large group of small animals which resemble each other in quite obvious ways. They all have a hard or shelly outside, which is made up of many joints or segments, and have jointed legs. They also have an apparatus round the mouth, consisting of jaws and jointed feelers for handling the food. Very often their bodies are divided into distinct regions, and the commonest type on land, the insect, often has wings.

Plate 1 shows examples of six of the better-known types of land Arthropods. They all show these distinguishing marks, but are still so different that they can be told apart at a glance. Any doubts as to the group into which an Arthropod should be placed can usually be settled by counting the legs and by noting the number of segments which make up the body.

KEY TO THE COMMONER LAND-LIVING ARTHROPODS

1. Legs
   - (a) more than eight in number 2
   - (b) eight or less in number 3

2. Body
   - (a) long and thin; (more than fourteen segments) .
                     MYRIAPOD (centipede or millipede)
   - (b) short; (fourteen segments or less) . . .
                              WOODLOUSE

3. Regions of body
   - (a) three regions, the middle one having six legs, and often wings . . . . . .
                              INSECT (p. 6)
   - (b) less than three regions; (eight legs) . . . 4

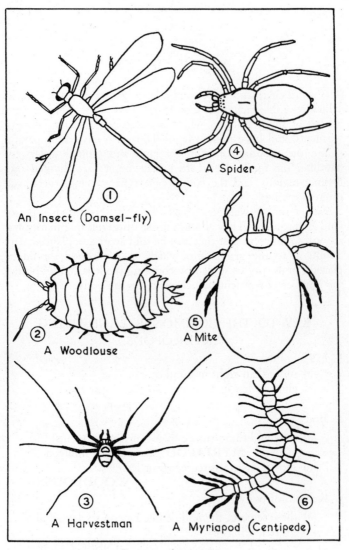

① An Insect (Damsel-fly)

② A Woodlouse

③ A Harvestman

④ A Spider

⑤ A Mite

⑥ A Myriapod (Centipede)

PLATE I. ARTHROPODS

4. Body

    (*a*) consisting of two regions, the front region, only,
        having legs.   .   .   **SPIDER** (p. 79)

    (*b*) not divided into regions   5

5. Legs

    (*a*) short   .   .   .   .   **MITE OR TICK**

    (*b*) long and spindly   .   **HARVESTMAN** (p. 112)

PRINCIPLES OF CLASSIFICATION

WE have already seen that it is sometimes quite easy to see the differences and similarities shown by animals. Classification involves noting all possible information of this sort, and grouping all the more similar animals together, and giving a "group name" to them as a whole.

For example, all animals are grouped into a dozen or more Phyla (singular, Phylum). The worms are put into one, the Annelida, the Arthropods are another, and all animals with backbones are put into a third, the Chordata. It is easy to see that different sorts of worms, say, earthworms and lugworms, are more like each other than they are like any Arthropod, and so must go into a different group. These Phyla are split into Classes. The insects form one Class of Arthropods, the Insecta; the spiders, mites and harvestmen all go into another, the Arachnida. The Isopods, or woodlice, are put with the Crustacea, together with crabs and shrimps. The Myriapoda, (centipedes and millipedes) are another Class. It can be seen that these various Classes are characterized by having six, eight, more than eight and very many legs respectively. There are other differences, seen better under a microscope.

Classes are split into Orders, as the Arachnida is split into spiders, harvestmen and mites (and others). Orders are split into Families. Very often the animals that are put into one Family bear considerable resemblance to each other, externally. An example of a Family of insects is the Vespidae, or wasps. Families, in turn, are split into genera (singular, genus) and genera are split into species. Each genus and each species has a scientific name. For example, in the Family of spiders, Thomisiidae, are several genera occurring in Britain, of which one is called *Xysticus*. Several species of this genus are known to scientists, some rare, some quite common. One of the best-known is *Xysticus cristatus*. The specific name is "*cristatus*," and should always be written with the generic name, and following

4

it. The complete name may be abbreviated thus, *X. cristatus* when there is no danger of confusion with another genus. Both names are normally printed in italics in the letterpress of books.

The principle of classification already referred to still holds good: all the species of *Xysticus* resemble each other more than they resemble any species of any other genus.

INTRODUCTION TO INSECTS

INSECTS may readily be distinguished from all other Arthropods by having wings. Even those insects which do not possess wings have only six legs, instead of the eight or more of other groups. (Details of wingless insects are given at the end of the "Key to the Orders of Insects.")

The body consists of three main regions, the *head*, the *thorax* and the *abdomen*.

The head carries a pair of eyes, the surfaces of which are made up of a number of facets. For this reason they are called *compound eyes*. The head also bears the *antennae* or feelers; their shape and length vary considerably, and should be carefully noted when identifying a specimen. On the under surface of the head are the *mouth-parts*, the *jaws* and other parts used in feeding.

The thorax consists of three segments, the second and third each carrying a pair of *wings*. On its lower side, each segment of the thorax has a pair of *legs*—making six legs in all. The legs are jointed, the large joint nearest the body being called the *thigh*. The next joint is the *shank*, followed by the *foot* which is itself made up of a variable number of joints. The foot ends in a *claw*, which does *not* count as a joint; e.g. the insect shown in Plate 2 has a foot consisting of three joints and a claw.

The abdomen has no legs or wings. There may be some projections at the rear end, usually concerned with egg-laying.

Insects are divided into Orders mainly on the differences in the wings and mouth-parts. Thus, the beetles have front-wings that are hardened into wing-cases; these are, strictly speaking, still wings. Most insects feed either by chewing vegetable matter or by tearing at the flesh of other animals, and typically their mouth-parts are shaped for biting. Important exceptions are seen in those which have a tube for sucking nectar (e.g. butterflies) or a "dagger" for piercing plants or the skin of animals (e.g. bugs and some flies). Orders are broken down into

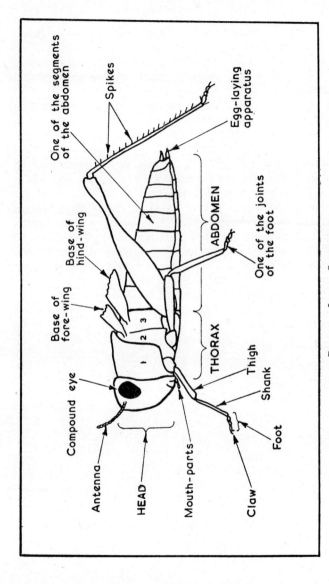

PLATE 2. INSECT STRUCTURE

Side view of grasshopper with wings removed. The numbers I, 2, 3 refer to the segments of the Thorax

Families largely on differences in the nature of the antennae, and on the number of joints in the foot.

This book is not concerned with details of the development of insects—consequently all immature stages are referred to simply as "larval stages."

All the illustrations, unless otherwise stated, were drawn looking down on the specimens from above. In some cases in order to save space, wings and legs are shown on one side only, or the legs have been omitted.

Information about collecting and setting of insects will be found in most of the books mentioned in the book list. Three practical hints may be given here—

1. Specimens should not be killed at once. Antennae are often seen more clearly in the living insect, and the insect's stance and behaviour are often characteristic.

2. When killed, the specimen is best examined impaled on a long pin. Only small and very delicate insects should be placed in alcohol.

3. Specimens should be examined in good light, and *close* to the light. This is particularly important when counting joints in feet or antennae.

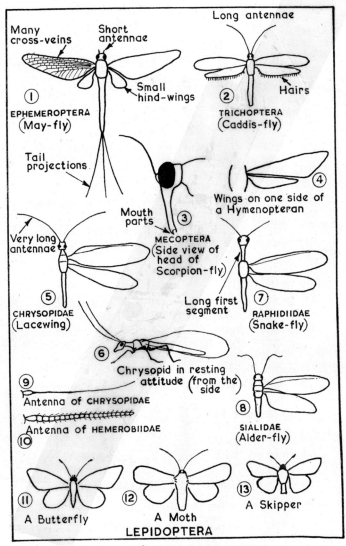

PLATE 3. INSECTS OF SEVERAL ORDERS

KEY TO THE ORDERS OF
BRITISH INSECTS

1. Wings

    (*a*) one pair only, no wing covering .   .
                          DIPTERA (True Flies, p. 70)

    (*b*) two distinct pairs,[1] *or* one pair of wings and one pair of wing coverings .   .   .   2

2. Wings

    (*a*) front pair *very* hard, forming a cover for the the hind pair[2] .   .   .   .   .
                  COLEOPTERA (Beetles, p. 38)

    (*b*) front pair not, or only slightly, harder than hind pair   3

3. Hind end of body

    (*a*) provided with pincers; (the body is flattened) .
                DERMAPTERA (Earwigs, p. 22)

    (*b*) without pincers   4

4. Body and wings

    (*a*) covered with scales which rub off .   .
        LEPIDOPTERA (Butterflies and moths, p. 37)

    (*b*) not covered thus   5

5. Hind end of body

    (*a*) provided with three long projections[3] [*see* Plate 3 (1)] .   .   .   .
            EPHEMEROPTERA (May-flies, p. 23)

[1] The hind-wings may be very small and difficult to separate from the fore-wings.

[2] The hard wing-cases do not always extend right to the end of the body (*see* Plates 6, 7 and 8).

[3] The long projections break off easily. Other features of may-flies are the very short antennae and the large number of cross-veins in the wings.

(b) not provided with three long projections *or* the
antennae are long 6

6. Appearance
    (a) *see* Plate 1 (1), (antennae very short) . .
        ODONATA (Dragon-flies and Damsel-flies,
        p. 24)
    (b) not as in Plate 1 (1) 7

7. Hind-wings
    (a) fringed with hairs (use hand lens); (fore-wings
        often darker than hind-wings [*see* Plate 3 (2)].
        TRICHOPTERA (Caddis-flies, p. 36)
    (b) without a fringe of hairs 8

8. Wings
    (a) flabby, both pairs about the same size and texture,
        many cross veins 9
    (b) not flabby, both pairs not similar in size and
        texture 10

9. Wings
    (a) folded flat along the back in the resting insect,
        brown patches on wings; (head projects
        downwards, examine insect sideways) [*see*
        Plate 3 (3)] . . . . . .
        MECOPTERA (Scorpion flies, p. 35)
    (b) folded roof-like along the back in the resting
        insect, head does not project far down [*see*
        Plate 3 (6)] . . . . . .
        NEUROPTERA (Lacewings etc., p. 33)

10. Wings
    (a) both pairs almost (or entirely) transparent, hind-
        wing smaller than fore-wing[1] [*see* Plate 3 (4)].
        HYMENOPTERA (Bees, wasps etc., p. 56)
    (b) features not as above 11

[1] The antennae of Hymenoptera are never very short. The following features
may be present: (a) a "waist" between thorax and abdomen, (b) black and yellow
striping, (c) a "sting" projecting from the rear.

11. Head

    (*a*) does not have biting jaws, but a "dagger-like" piercing organ which is held against the under side of the body [*see* Plate 5 (1) and (2)], (examine insect sideways[1]) . . . .
               HEMIPTERA (Bugs etc., p. 25).

    (*b*) has no "dagger" 12

12. Fore-wings

    (*a*) not very hard; (hind-legs very long, all legs bearing large spikes on the shank; general appearance of insect as in Plate 2 or Plate 4) .
        ORTHOPTERA (Grasshoppers etc., p. 14)

    (*b*) usually hard; (insect not having the features mentioned above, *see* p. 9[2]) . . .
            COLEOPTERA (Beetles, p. 38)

Wingless Insects. Many of the orders mentioned above include some wingless members. They occur chiefly among the Hemiptera, Hymenoptera and Orthoptera, and may be placed in the appropriate order by examining them for the characteristic features—

    (*a*) Presence of a "dagger" . . . . .
           HEMIPTERA (p. 25), e.g. green-fly.

    (*b*) Presence of a "waist" . . . . . .
        HYMENOPTERA (p. 56), e.g. ants and some wasps.

    (*c*) Presence of strong hind-legs used for jumping, or of many strong spikes on the long legs . . .
        ORTHOPTERA (p. 14), e.g. many grasshoppers and cockroaches.

There are also some wingless insects which do not belong to any of the preceding orders—

    (*a*) *Springtails.* Very small insects found in almost every

---

[1] The fore-wing is usually, though not always, harder than the hind-wing and forms a cover for it.

Lesser water-boatmen, which live in the water, have only a very short "dagger."

situation. They are able to leap by means of appendages at the end of the body. The leaping can be quite easily watched if a specimen is caught in a tube. The body is generally elongated and the antennae easy to see.

(*b*) *Silver-fish*. Nearly 6 mm long with long antennae and projections at the end of the body. They live in houses, often near flour, and scurry along the ground on very short legs. Silvery appearance.

(*c*) *Fleas*. Parasites on the skin of mammals and birds. The body is short and flattened sideways. The legs are long and the antennae very short. They can jump by means of their legs.

ORDER **ORTHOPTERA**

THE Orthoptera as a group are relatively unspecialized and show the general features of insects quite clearly. For this reason they are often used to illustrate the "typical insect," but such a term must of course be treated with the utmost reserve. Even within so compact a group as the Orthoptera there exist distinct differences of structure and habit.

KEY TO THE FAMILIES OF ORTHOPTERA

1. Legs

   (*a*) all more or less equal in length, all bearing strong spikes [*see* Plate 4 (1)] . . . . .
                    FAMILY *BLATTIDAE* (p. 16)

   (*b*) hind pair much longer than the others and having bigger spikes 2

2. Antennae

   (*a*) shorter than the body 3

   (*b*) as long as, or longer than, the body [*see* Plate 4 (5) and (7)] 5

3. Fore-limbs

   (*a*) massive; (a burrowing insect) [*see* Plate 4 (4)] .
                    FAMILY *GRYLLOTALPIDAE* (p. 16)

   (*b*) slender 4

4. Thorax

   (*a*) extends backwards as a lobe over the wings and wing-covers [*see* Plate 4 (6)] . . . .
                    FAMILY *TETRIGIDAE* (p. 17)

   (*b*) does not extend backwards [*see* Plate 2] . .
                    FAMILY *ACRIDIDAE* (p. 17)

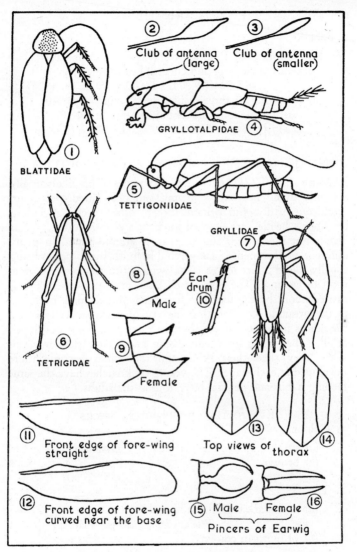

② Club of antenna (large)

③ Club of antenna (smaller)

GRYLLOTALPIDAE ④

① BLATTIDAE

⑤ TETTIGONIIDAE

GRYLLIDAE ⑦

⑧ Male

Ear drum ⑩

⑥ TETRIGIDAE

⑨ Female

⑪ Front edge of fore-wing straight

⑬ ⑭ Top views of thorax

⑫ Front edge of fore-wing curved near the base

⑮ Male   Female ⑯
Pincers of Earwig

PLATE 4. ORTHOPTERA AND DERMAPTERA
Figs. 4, 5, 8 and 9 are shown from the left-hand side

5. Foot

    (a) consisting of four joints; (egg-laying apparatus
       of female long and curved) [see Plate 4 (5)] .
          FAMILY *TETTIGONIIDAE* (p. 18)
    (b) consisting of three joints; (egg-laying apparatus
       of female long and absolutely straight) [see Plate
       4 (7)] .   . FAMILY *GRYLLIDAE* (p. 20)

NOTES ON THE FAMILIES OF ORTHOPTERA

FAMILY *BLATTIDAE*. The Cockroaches. This is essentially
a family living in warm climates, and only three species are
found out of doors in Britain, though other species, including
the "black beetle" are pests of kitchens and storehouses. Their
diet is not specialized, and they are therefore found in many
different environments. They avoid light, the field species being
usually found under leaves. The wings of the females are often
short or lacking. The eggs are enclosed in an egg-case which is
carried about by the female, often partially extruded, until laid
in the ground. On hatching the young cockroaches resemble
the adults in most features, but their wings are not developed
at all. The young grow, increasing in size at certain intervals
when they shed their skins, and the wings become more
developed at each stage. The young cockroaches have the same
feeding habits and general behaviour as the adults.

KEY TO THE OUT-OF-DOORS SPECIES

1. Colour

    (a) straw .   .   .   .   *Ectobius lividus*
    (b) brown 2

2. Thorax

    (a) with dark region in the middle   .   .   .
            Ectobius lapponicus [see Plate 4 (1)]
    (b) of uniform colour .   .   . *Ectobius panzeri*

FAMILY *GRYLLOTALPIDAE*. There is only one species,
Gryllotalpa gryllotalpa, which is found locally in Southern

England, notably in the New Forest. It burrows under the roots of trees by means of its very powerful fore-limbs, whence its name, the "mole-cricket."

FAMILY *TETRIGIDAE*. We have two common species.

Tetrix vittata [*see* Plate 4 (6)]. The thorax lobe does not project beyond the end of the body.

Tetrix subulata. The thorax lobe extends well beyond the end of the body. Less common than the previous species.

FAMILY *ACRIDIDAE*. To this family belong the familiar "Shorthorn grasshoppers," of which there are six common species. All feed on grass. They are able to leap by means of their powerful hind-legs. The females lay their eggs, enclosed in a rough covering, in the ground during late summer. The eggs remain there throughout the winter and hatch in late spring, the young resembling the adults except for differences in size and wing development. They grow to the adult condition in two or three months, and having mated and laid their eggs, die in the autumn. The familiar chirping sound is produced by rubbing the rough side of the thigh against a ridge on the fore-wing. Shorthorns can detect sound by means of "ear-drums" on either side of the body, on the first segment of the abdomen. The sexes may be distinguished by examining the end of the abdomen, which, in the male is rounded [*see* Plate 4 (8)]; in the female the sharp points of the egg-laying apparatus are visible [*see* Plate 4 (9)]. In case of doubt the end of the abdomen should be gently squeezed, when the apparatus will be protruded if the specimen is a female.

KEY TO THE COMMONER SPECIES

1. Antennae

    (*a*) end not club shaped [*see* Plate 2] . . . 2
    (*b*) end club shaped [*see* Plate 4 (2) and (3)] . . 5

2. Fore-wing

    (*a*) front edge straight [*see* Plate 4 (11)] . . . 3
    (*b*) front edge curved near the base [*see* Plate 4 (12)]
        or wings much reduced 4

3. Front of head

    (a) a vertical ridge between the eyes   .   .   .
                                            Omocestus viridulus

    (b) no such ridge.   .   .   *Omocestus ventralis*

4. Upper surface of thorax

    (a) sides bending inwards [see Plate 4 (13)]   .   .
                                          Chorthippus bicolor

    (b) sides almost straight [see Plate 4 (14)].   .   .
                                        Chorthippus parallelus

5. Antennae

    (a) club large, tipped with white [see Plate 4 (2)]   .
                                          Gomphocerus rufus

    (b) club smaller, no white tips [see Plate 4 (3)].   .
                                        Myrmeleotettix maculatus

Chorthippus bicolor is probably the commonest of our grass-hoppers. Its colour is very variable and specimens often match the background closely. The underside of the thorax is much more hairy than in other species. *Chorthippus parallelus* too is very common. Both sexes have short wings but in the females, which are more numerous than the males, they are so short as to be scarcely visible. Of the two species of *Omocestus*, *O. viridulus* is the more common, and may be further distinguished by its more greenish colour and by having the shank of the hind-legs yellowish rather than red. *Gomphocerus rufus* may, with practice, be identified at a glance by the long clubbed antennae, and *Myrmeleotettix maculatus* by its very small size.

FAMILY *TETTIGONIIDAE*. The "Longhorn grass-hoppers." Unlike the shorthorns they do not leap but move slowly in the grass or on trees and bushes. Many species have shortened wings, or lack them entirely. These produce no sound, but in the winged forms the males chirp vigorously by rubbing together the bases of the fore-wings. Their "ear-drums" are situated on the thick part of the shank of the fore-legs [see Plate 4 (10)]. The eggs are laid separately. The long blades of the egg-laying apparatus form a tube which the female inserts into plant tissues and the egg travels down the tube. The hatching of the egg and development of the young is similar to that of the shorthorns. We have nine native species, only six of which are at all likely to be seen.

KEY TO THE COMMONER SPECIES

(*Note.* Lengths do *not* include the egg-laying apparatus)

1. Length
   (*a*) over 38 mm 2
   (*b*) much less, about 13 mm 3

2. Length
   (*a*) 43 mm or more; (bright green) . . .
   Tettigonia viridissima
   (*b*) shorter; (brown or greenish brown). . .
   Decticus verrucivorus

3. Colour
   (*a*) dark brown . . . *Pholidoptera griseoaptera*
   (*b*) green or mainly green 4

4. Colour
   (*a*) wholly green *Meconema thalassina* [*see* Plate 4 (5)]
   (*b*) not wholly green 5

5. Wings
   (*a*) present . . . . *Conocephalus dorsalis*
   (*b*) not present; (body finely stippled with black) .
   Leptophyes punctatissima

Tettigonia viridissima has wings extending backwards well beyond the end of the abdomen. Its egg-laying apparatus is almost as long as the body and is almost straight. In some parts of Southern England it may be heard chirping in the evening. It may be partly carnivorous in habit. In *Decticus verrucivorus* the wings are no longer than the body, and the egg-laying apparatus is long and has a gentle upward curve. It differs from the other longhorns in laying its eggs not in plant tissue but in the ground. *Pholidoptera griseoaptera* is one of our commonest longhorns. Its wings are very small, about 2 mm in the male and scarcely visible in the female. It is found on grasses. *Meconema thalassina* is a beautiful insect with delicate green colour and a slender body. The egg-laying apparatus is slender and slightly curved. It is not uncommon on oak trees. *Leptophyes punctatissima* is quite common on trees and shrubs. In the male the upper surface of the thorax is light brown. The egg-laying apparatus is short and strongly curved. *Conocephalus dorsalis* occurs in marshes and other damp places. It is not common.

FAMILY *GRYLLIDAE*. The Crickets. These insects vary considerably in their choice of habitat, some living in close contact with man and others partly underground in fields and woods. They resemble longhorns in their manner of growth and in general appearance, but have only three joints in the foot, a long and very straight egg-laying apparatus, and the wings lie flat along the abdomen instead of sloping. They produce sound by rubbing the rough right fore-wing over the left. We have three species.

KEY TO THE SPECIES

(*Note*. Lengths do *not* include the egg-laying apparatus)

1. Colour

    (*a*) glossy black; (over 20 mm) .   .   .   .
                            Gryllus campestris [*see* Plate 4 (7)]

    (*b*) not glossy black   2

2. Size

    (*a*) about 18 mm long; (wings fully developed) .
                            Gryllulus domesticus

    (*b*) much smaller; (wings very short) .   .   .
                            Nemobius sylvestris

Gryllulus domesticus, the "cricket on the hearth," is the only one which is at all common, and is a minor pest of kitchens and other places where food is stored. It feeds on almost any debris, and lays its eggs in crevices in buildings. It is often heard chirping at night, but is not easy to find. *Gryllus campestris*, the field cricket, makes a burrow for itself on sunny banks. It chirps continuously by day during the summer in some parts of Southern England. The eggs are laid in the ground. *Nemobius sylvestris* is found only in the New Forest and the Isle of Wight. It does not burrow but lives under leaves.

ORDER **DERMAPTERA**
(Earwigs)

WE have but one common species of Earwig, *Forficula auricularia*. It has large hind-wings folded under the small fore-wings and can fly well, but since flight usually takes place at night it is rarely observed. It lives on the ground in concealed places under stones, or under the bark of trees. The sexes may be distinguished by the shape of the pincers, those of the male being the more strongly curved [*see* Plate 4 (15) and (16)]. The females show a certain care of the young, an unusual feature among insects. The eggs are laid in a nest made in the soil and the female cleans and stands guard over them until they hatch, and for some time after. The young resemble the adults but lack wings. They grow in five or six stages, shedding their skin each time.

ORDER **EPHEMEROPTERA**
(May-flies)

THE larvae of may-flies live in water (sometimes for several years), and shortly after emerging the adults mate in flight. This usually occurs when they swarm in huge numbers in the evening. They perform a kind of dance over the water, and many are taken by fish. The adults are rarely found far from water; they do not feed and live for only a few days—some for only a few hours. The order is of no economic importance.

There are forty-six British species, some very small. The two described below are the commonest of the large species.

Ephemera vulgata. Wing span 35 mm. The wings are mottled with large patches of brown.

Ephemera danica. Wing span 35 mm. The brown patches on the wings are less prominent than in *E. vulgata*, and, on the hind-wings, are reduced to a single speck.

ORDER **ODONATA**

(Dragonflies)

THE Odonata are fast-flying insects which seize their prey on the wing. Associated with this habit they possess very large eyes and their legs are provided with powerful spikes and claws, while their antennae are small. (Contrast this feature with the antennae of insects which "feel" their way.) The adults are often found near water. The eggs are laid in the water, and the larval stages all take place there. The order is of no economic importance, except that the dragon-flies kill large numbers of insects many of which are harmful. There are forty-two British species.

All Odonata are very similar in structure, and it is therefore difficult to give features by which they may readily be divided into families. Genera are still more difficult to define. Simple keys are based on colour[1]. (*See* book list.)

There are two Sub-orders—

Both pairs of wings similar in size and shape; eyes not excessively large and not meeting in the middle of the head

SUB-ORDER **ZYGOPTERA**

Hind-wings broader than the fore-wings; eyes very large indeed and meeting in the middle of the head .

SUB-ORDER **ANISOPTERA**

The Zygoptera or damsel-flies [*see* Plate 1 (1)] have slender bodies and are not strong fliers, while the Anisoptera or dragon-flies (which are the more numerous) are more powerfully built and fly very fast.

[1] The vivid colours fade quickly after death. Do not kill your specimens in the field but place them in long thin tubes so that they cannot damage their wings.

ORDER **HEMIPTERA**
(Bugs)

THE characteristic feature of this order is the "dagger-like" nature of the mouth-parts. They form a tube with a pointed end which the insect thrusts into the plant on which it feeds, and then sucks its juice. This may harm the plant in several ways, and the Hemiptera are therefore of great economic importance. A few feed on the body fluids of animals, chiefly of other insects.

The Hemiptera may first be divided into two Sub-orders—

Antennae short (unless the insect is very small and delicate); head fits closely on to the thorax without a "chin" region [*see* Plate 5 (1), examine insect sideways]; fore-wing of similar texture all over; insect never aquatic.

SUB-ORDER **HOMOPTERA**

Antennae prominent (unless insect is aquatic); there is a "chin" region [*see* Plate 5 (2)]; fore-wing consists of a firm opaque region near the base and a delicate semi-transparent region near the tip (pull wing out sideways) [*see* Plate 5 (3)]

SUB-ORDER **HETEROPTERA**

KEY TO THE FAMILIES OF HOMOPTERA

There are 900 British species, of which about 400 are Aphididae.

1. Antennae

   (*a*) inconspicuous [*see* Plate 5 (1)] 2
   (*b*) prominent 5

2. Hind-leg

   (*a*) shank carries no spikes . . . . .
                FAMILY *CICADIDAE* (p. 29)
   (*b*) shank carries some or many spikes [*see* Plate 5 (4) and (5)] 3

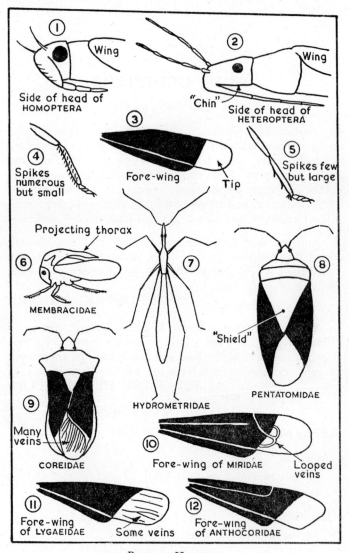

PLATE 5. HEMIPTERA
Fig. 6 is shown from a side view

3. Spikes
    (*a*) numerous but small [*see* Plate 5 (4)]   .   .   .   4
    (*b*) very few, but large [*see* Plate 5 (5)]   .   .   .
                       FAMILY *CERCOPIDAE* (p. 29)

4. Thorax
    (*a*) projects far back and upwards [*see* Plate 5 (6)]   .
                       FAMILY *MEMBRACIDAE* (p. 30)
    (*b*) flattened, not pointed   .   .   .   .   .
                       FAMILY *JASSIDAE* (p. 30)

5. Body of insect
    (*a*) covered in a white mealy powder   .   .   .
                       FAMILY *ALEYRODIDAE* (p. 30)
    (*b*) not covered in a white mealy powder   .   .   6

6. Antennae
    (*a*) consisting of ten joints (a jumping insect)   .   .
                       FAMILY *CHERMIDAE* (p. 30)
    (*b*) consisting of from three to six joints (not a
        jumping insect)   .   .   .   .   .
                       FAMILY *APHIDIDAE* (p. 30)

KEY TO THE FAMILIES OF HETEROPTERA

There are 500 British species. The division of this sub-order into families depends partly on features of the fore-wing. These features are not really difficult to see if the fore-wing is extended sideways and examined with a hand lens in good light.

1. Situation
    (*a*) on land or on water surface; (antennae of four or
        five prominent joints)   .   .   .   2
    (*b*) actually *in* the water; (antennae difficult to see).   10

2. Dagger
    (*a*) short and stout, curved away from the body
        when not in use   .   .   .   .
                       FAMILY *REDUVIIDAE* (p. 30)
    (*b*) long and slender, lying close against the body
        when not in use [*see* Plate 5 (2)]   .   .   .   3

3. Situation

>   (*a*) on water surface 4
>   (*b*) on land 6

4. Body

>   (*a*) long and thin [*see* Plate 5 (7)] . . . .
>   FAMILY *HYDROMETRIDAE* (p. 31)
>   (*b*) not so greatly elongated 5

5. Middle-legs

>   (*a*) half-way between fore and hind-legs . .
>   FAMILY *VELIIDAE* (p. 31)
>   (*b*) nearer the hind-legs . . . . .
>   FAMILY *GERRIDAE* (p. 31)

6. Antennae

>   (*a*) consisting of five joints[1]; (thorax extends far
>   back between the wings like a shield) [*see*
>   Plate 5 (8)] . . . . . .
>   FAMILY *PENTATOMIDAE* (p. 31)
>   (*b*) consisting of four joints; (no shield extending
>   far back between the wings) . . . 7

7. Wing-tip

>   (*a*) having many veins; (thorax and hind-body
>   broader than the wings) [*see* Plate 5 (9)] .
>   FAMILY *COREIDAE* (p. 31)
>   (*b*) having only a few veins; (hind-body not much
>   broader than wings; insect often small. . 8

8. Veins of wing-tip

>   (*a*) one or two looped veins [*see* Plate 5 (10)]; body
>   often elongated and legs delicate). . .
>   FAMILY *MIRIDAE* (p. 31)
>   (*b*) either absent or not looped 9

---

[1] The first joint of the antennae of Pentatomidae may be rather small, but is plainly visible with a hand lens.

9. Veins of wing-tip

    (a) some present [see Plate 5 (11)] .   .   .   .
                        FAMILY *LYGAEIDAE* (p. 32)

    (b) none present [see Plate 5 (12)]; (very small insects) .   .   .   .   .   .
               FAMILY *ANTHOCORIDAE* (p. 32)

10. Abdomen

    (a) with a long tube projecting from the end   .
                        FAMILY *NEPIDAE* (p. 32)

    (b) no long tube   11

11. Dagger

    (a) long; (back sharply ridged; insect swims on its back) .   .   .   .   .   .
               FAMILY *NOTONECTIDAE* (p. 32)

    (b) scarcely present; (back flat; insect swims right way up) .   .   .   .   .   .
               FAMILY *CORIXIDAE* (p. 32)

NOTES ON THE FAMILIES OF HEMIPTERA

FAMILY *CICADIDAE*. Most members of this family live in warmer climates, and our one species *Cicadetta montana* is rare and found only in the New Forest. Their life-history is interesting; the larvae live for many years underground, sucking juices from plant roots. The adults are good fliers, and the males produce a singing noise which is heard by the females and thus serves to bring the sexes together. To this family belong the cigales of Southern France made famous by the writings of Fabre.

FAMILY *CERCOPIDAE*. Frog hoppers or cuckoo spit insects. They are numerous and responsible for the masses of foam often to be found on plants in the summer especially where leaves are joined to the stem. The adults are active and leap readily. The eggs are laid in plant tissue and the larvae produce the foam which completely surrounds them. The purpose of the foam is not really understood—it certainly does not always act as a protection. *Philaenus leucophthalmus*, the common

cuckoo spit insect, 9 mm with the wings folded, brown with
distinct patches of very light brown. *Cercopis vulnerata*, 10 mm
with wings folded, black with three large red areas on the fore-
wings. Quite common.

FAMILY *MEMBRACIDAE*. Thorn insects. The pointed
elongation of the thorax is very prominent in some tropical
species, and when resting on branches of thorny plants the
insects are almost indistinguishable from the thorns. There are
two British species of which only *Centrotus cornutus* [*see* Plate
5 (6)] is at all common.

FAMILY *JASSIDAE*. A very numerous family of hopping
insects, often called leaf hoppers. Among the commonest is
Euacanthus interruptus, 9 mm with wings folded, black with
green streaks. *Ledra aurita*, 15 to 17 mm with wings folded,
greenish, the sides of the thorax extend outwards giving the
appearance of "ears." Found on oak.

FAMILY *ALEYRODIDAE*. White flies. Very small bugs.
They are covered in a mealy white powder (hence also called
powder wings), and exude a sticky liquid, "honey-dew." They
occur together in large numbers on foliage.

FAMILY *CHERMIDAE*. Jumping plant lice. Small bugs
which can leap by means of their large hind-legs. They are
often found near honey-dew which is exuded by their larvae.
Chermes mali is a pest of apple trees.

FAMILY *APHIDIDAE*. Green-fly and black-fly. Among
the most numerous of all insects. Wings are usually found only
in the males which are much less common than the females—
indeed among some genera no males have ever been recorded.
The females can lay eggs which develop without being fertilized
by the males. Aphids occur in vast numbers, reproducing many
times during the season, and so are serious agricultural pests.
They secrete honey-dew, see above. *Eriosoma lanigerum*, woolly
aphis, producing "American" blight. On apple trees it exudes
a waxy substance resembling cotton wool. The insects can be
found among the strands of the "wool." *Adelges abietis*, pro-
duces galls on spruce. The galls appear on the stems in the place
of needles, the bugs living inside the galls.

FAMILY *REDUVIIDAE*. Assassin bugs etc. The short

powerful "dagger" is used for stabbing other insects—an unusual habit among the Hemiptera. *Reduvius personatus*, 18 mm, dark brown, rather rare, attacks man. *Nabis lativentris* mimics ants; part of the abdomen has transparent sides, giving the appearance of a thin ant-like waist.

FAMILY *HYDROMETRIDAE*. One species only, *Hydrometra stagnorum*, the water measurer [*see* Plate 5 (7)], 12 mm, wingless. It walks slowly on the water surface.

FAMILY *VELIIDAE*. There is only one species of any size. *Velia currens*, 6 to 8 mm, usually wingless.

Family *GERRIDAE*. Pond skaters. These bugs skim fast over the surface of the water. The underside of the body is covered with a layer of silvery hairs which are unwettable.

The following is a rough guide to the commoner species. *Gerris najas*, 13 to 17 mm, usually wingless. *G. thoracicus*, 10 to 12 mm, hinder part of thorax yellowish brown. *G. gibbifer*, 10 to 13 mm, hinder part of thorax dark. *G. lacustris*, much smaller, 8 to 10 mm.

FAMILY *PENTATOMIDAE*. Shield bugs. A large family whose members closely resemble each other. In a few the "shield" formed by the thorax is so large that it almost conceals the wings. *Elasmucha grisea*, 10 mm, head and thorax reddish brown, fore-wings and tips darker, sides of abdomen orange with black marks project slightly beyond the wings.

FAMILY *COREIDAE*. Not a very large family. *Coreus marginatus*, 14 mm, head, thorax and fore-wings dull brown, second and third joints of antennae red.

FAMILY *MIRIDAE*. An important family of plant pests, also known as the Capsids. They are numerous, and often small, but can usually be recognized by the two looped veins in the wing tip. This feature is clearly visible, even in the field, provided the wing is extended and examined with a hand lens. *Harpocera thoracica*, 5 mm, thorax brownish black with a white line running down the middle, fore-wings very pale with areas of darker brown especially near the tip of the thicker region, the whole insect has a shiny appearance and an oval shape. *Stenodema* (many species), long slender and parallel sided, fore-wing light green, flat bodied.

FAMILY *LYGAEIDAE*. A large family. *Heterogaster urticae*, 8 mm, head and thorax black, fore-wing grey. Common on nettles.

FAMILY *ANTHOCORIDAE*. A family of very small bugs.

FAMILY *NEPIDAE*. Both our species are fairly common and should be sought at the bottom of ponds. The front legs can be used for grasping, and the insects have a scorpion-like appearance. They are able to breathe under water, the end of the abdominal tube being held just above the surface. *Nepa cinerea*, the water scorpion, 10 mm not including the tube. *Ranatra linearis*, the water stick insect, 30 mm not including the tube.

FAMILY *NOTONECTIDAE*. Large water-boatmen. Very active bugs which can inflict a persistently painful wound with the long "dagger." They are carnivorous, and should never be kept with other insects or small animals in an aquarium. We have four species. *Notonecta obliqua*, 16 mm, fore-wing black except for two large streaks of yellow near the base. *N. viridis*, 14 mm, fore-wing pale with a darker strip round the outer edge and the base of the transparent region, general colour of the body and especially of the legs bright green. *N. maculata*, 14 mm, fore-wing reddish with dark brown mottling and a paler region near the base. *N. glauca*, 14 mm, fore-wing pale with a dark strip along part of the outer edge.

FAMILY *CORIXIDAE*. Lesser water-boatmen. In this family the "dagger" is so short that it is scarcely noticeable, and instead of stabbing their prey, as do the species of *Notonecta* (above), the species of *Corixa* suck small particles into the mouth as they swim near the bottom. The family is large, and its members are to be found in most ponds and streams. Although mostly of small size they are by no means impossible to identify (*see* book list) and they provide suitable material for much simple work on ecology and behaviour.

ORDER **NEUROPTERA**

THIS is a large order, but has only about fifty British representatives. Among the characteristic features are the large flabby wings which have many veins, and also the delicate nature of the abdomen which often shrivels when the insect is pinned. At rest the wings are held folded roof-like over the body as in Plate 3 (6).

The following is a key to the commoner families.

KEY TO THE FAMILIES OF NEUROPTERA

1. Antennae
   (*a*) nobbly [*see* Plate 3 (10)]; (insect brown) . .
              FAMILY *HEMEROBIIDAE* (p. 34)
   (*b*) not nobbly; (insect brown or green) . . 2

2. First segment of thorax
   (*a*) long, so that the head appears to be on a long "neck" [*see* Plate 3 (7)] . . . . .
              FAMILY *RAPHIDIIDAE* (p. 34)
   (*b*) not particularly long 3

3. Wing span
   (*a*) over 40 mm, wings spotted . . . .
              FAMILY *OSMYLIDAE* (p. 34)
   (*b*) less than 40 mm, or wings not spotted . . 4

4. Colour
   (*a*) green or brown; long slender antennae [*see* Plate 3 (9)]; [*see* plate 3 (5) and (6)] . .
              FAMILY *CHRYSOPIDAE* (p. 34)
   (*b*) brown; (antennae shorter) 5

5. Wing span

    (a) over 22 mm [see Plate 3 (8)] . . . .
                    FAMILY *SIALIDAE* (p. 34)
    (b) much less . FAMILY *SISYRIDAE* (p. 34)

NOTES ON THE FAMILIES OF NEUROPTERA

FAMILY *SIALIDAE*. Alder flies. There are two British species. The adults are weak fliers; their wings are light brown with large dark veins. The eggs are laid in water and most of the larval development takes place there.

FAMILY *RAPHIDIIDAE*. Snake flies. The first segment of the thorax is not firmly joined to the second but is free to move upon it, which makes the insect appear to have a very long neck. Snake flies are carnivorous. They lay their eggs under the bark of trees, for which purpose the female is equipped with a long egg-laying organ.

FAMILY *HEMEROBIIDAE*. Brown lacewings. About thirty British species. Can always be distinguished from the Chrysopidae (below) by the nobbly antennae. Apart from this feature they resemble the Chrysopidae in general structure and habits.

Family *OSMYLIDAE*. Only one British species, *Osmylus fulvicephalus*, the wings are translucent but partially marked with grey. Found near water, but not common.

FAMILY *SISYRIDAE*. Inconspicuous insects. The eggs are laid on plants overhanging water. The larvae live in the water.

FAMILY *CHRYSOPIDAE*. Green lacewings. The adults are to be found on foliage during the summer. One species, *Chrysopa carnea*, survives the winter in the adult stage and often hibernates in houses, which accounts for the occasional appearance of a lacewing indoors in mid-winter. Lacewings are common and easily caught, having poor powers of flight. The eggs are usually laid on vegetation. The larvae feed voraciously on aphids (green-fly, p. 30) and on other bugs and are an important natural check on these pests. There are twelve British species of *Chrysopa* (green colour) and two of *Nathanica* (brown colour). All the species resemble each other closely.

ORDER **MECOPTERA**
(Scorpion flies)

THE scorpion flies have poor powers of flight. They are carnivorous but clearly unable to capture fast moving prey. The end of the abdomen of the male bears a large club-like structure (part of the genital organs) which is held curled forwards over the abdomen, whence the popular name. There are two common species.

Panorpa communis. Wing span about 30 mm. The brown colour on the wings is in broad bands.

Panorpa germanica. Wing span about 25 mm. The brown colour is present in the form of small specks.

ORDER **TRICHOPTERA**
(Caddis-flies)

THESE insects are related to the Lepidoptera (below) though there is not much danger of confusion. The dark appearance of the fore-wings is due to the presence of hairs which do not rub off as easily as the scales of Lepidoptera. The hind edge of the hind-wing bears a fringe of hairs which may be quite short but always plainly visible if the specimen is examined with a hand lens in front of the light. Although there are 200 British species the adults are not often seen. They are weak fliers and spend most of their time resting. They take scarcely any food. It is unusual to find them far from water. The larvae live in water and are the well-known caddis-fly larvae. The order is of no economic importance.

ORDER **LEPIDOPTERA**
(Butterflies and Moths)

THE members of this order are very similar in structure and would be difficult to name were it not for the colour patterns produced by the arrangement of the scales on the wings. The families are distinguished mainly by means of the veins of the wings, which become visible when the scales are rubbed off, but this is obviously a difficult feature to use and it is not proposed to suggest a classification in this book. There are many books which provide pictures by means of which the insects can be identified (*see* book list). The popular distinction into butterflies and moths is rough and ready. "Butterflies" [*see* Plate 3 (11)] have slender antennae slightly thickened at the end, hold their wings vertically above the body when resting, have comparatively slender bodies and usually fly in the daytime. "Moths" [*see* Plate 3 (12)] have antennae of various shapes (but never quite of the butterfly type), fold their wings in many different ways, usually have broad bodies and fly after dark. None of these features is definite except for the antennal feature of butterflies. The Skippers [*see* Plate 3 (13)] are included among the butterflies but have certain moth-like characters.

The order has over 2,000 British species and is of the utmost importance, both economically and in nature. It offers many possibilities for school field-work, e.g. protective colouration, methods of overwintering, attraction to flowers of certain colour and scent, importance of caterpillar attack on crops, genetical variation etc. Suggestions for work of this description will spring from a perusal of the books listed in the "General" section of the insect book list.

ORDER **COLEOPTERA**
(Beetles)

THIS is the largest order of insects, though not the most numerous one in Britain where there are about 3,700 species. They are found in almost every habitat and are extremely varied in form. Characteristically the fore-wings are hard, and form cases which protect the hind-wings and cover the abdomen when closed. In some families, however, the wing-cases are soft, and in others they are so short that much of the abdomen is exposed.

KEY TO THE FAMILIES OF COLEOPTERA

The classification used here divides the order into thirty families. The key is not difficult to use provided that the antennae are carefully examined; this calls for patience with the living beetle and skill with the set specimen. Antennae are described as "clubbed" if there is a distinct lump at the end. "Elbowed" means that they are distinctly bent at some point along their length. Where there is doubt concerning these features the key will usually be found to work both ways, so if the final identification seems questionable then go back to the doubtful feature and try it the other way.

1. Situation
    - (*a*) in water or on the surface 2
    - (*b*) neither in water nor on the surface . . . 6

2. Behaviour
    - (*a*) swimming fast in circles on the surface, often in large numbers [*see* Plate 6 (1)] . . .
        FAMILY *GYRINIDAE* (p. 48)
    - (*b*) not behaving as above 3

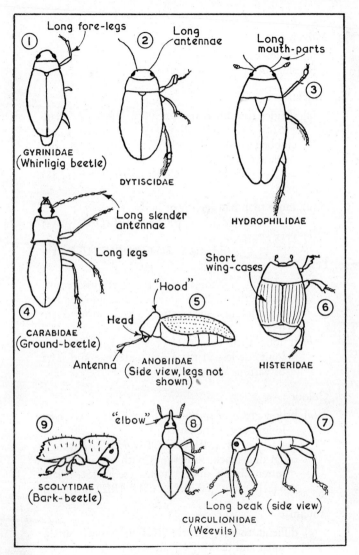

1. Long fore-legs
GYRINIDAE
(Whirligig beetle)

2. Long antennae
DYTISCIDAE

3. Long mouth-parts
HYDROPHILIDAE

4. Long slender antennae
Long legs
CARABIDAE
(Ground-beetle)

5. "Hood"
Head
Antenna
ANOBIIDAE
(Side view, legs not shown)

6. Short wing-cases
HISTERIDAE

9. SCOLYTIDAE
(Bark-beetle)

8. "elbow"

7. Long beak (side view)
CURCULIONIDAE
(Weevils)

PLATE 6. COLEOPTERA I

3. Movement

    (*a*) rapid, very good swimmers   4
    (*b*) sluggish, poor swimmers   5

4. Antennae

    (*a*) slender (mouth-parts not very long) [*see* Plate
        6 (2)]   . FAMILY *DYTISCIDAE* (p. 47)
    (*b*) clubbed (some mouth-parts very long) [*see*
        Plate 6 (3)]   .   .   .   .   .
            FAMILY *HYDROPHILIDAE* (p. 48)

5. Antennae

    (*a*) more than half length of body   .   .   .
            FAMILY *CHRYSOMELIDAE* (p. 54)
    (*b*) very short   .   .   .   .   .   .
            FAMILY *HYGROBIIDAE* (p. 47)

6. Legs

    (*a*) very long, five joints in *all* the feet; (insect runs
        fast on the ground; antennae long and slender;
        jaws usually sharp and curved). [*See* Plate
        6 (4)]   7
    (*b*) if long then *not* used for rapid running, five
        joints or less in the feet; (antennae and jaws
        of various shapes)   8

7. Colour

    (*a*) bright green or spotted with yellow; (jaws very
        long, curved and sharp)   .   .   .
            FAMILY *CICINDELIDAE* (p. 47)
    (*b*) often dull black, sometimes with metallic hues;
        (often living under stones etc.). [*See* Plate
        6 (4)]   . FAMILY *CARABIDAE* (p. 47)

8. Antennae

    (*a*) difficult to see; (insect lives in wood; small,
        squat and dark) [*see* Plate 6 (9)]   .   .
            FAMILY *SCOLYTIDAE* (p. 55)
    (*b*) easily seen   9

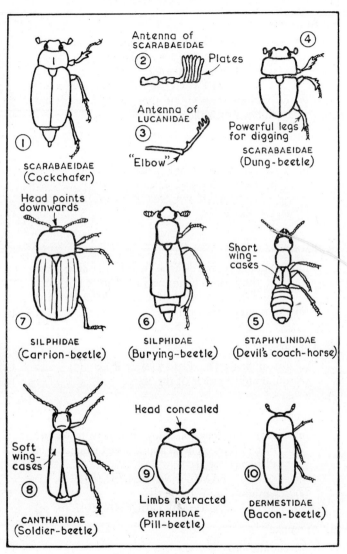

Antenna of
SCARABAEIDAE
② — Plates

Antenna of
LUCANIDAE
③
"Elbow"

④

Powerful legs
for digging
SCARABAEIDAE
(Dung-beetle)

①
SCARABAEIDAE
(Cockchafer)

Head points
downwards

Short
wing-
cases

⑦
SILPHIDAE
(Carrion-beetle)

⑥
SILPHIDAE
(Burying-beetle)

⑤
STAPHYLINIDAE
(Devil's coach-horse)

Soft
wing-
cases

Head concealed

⑨
Limbs retracted
BYRRHIDAE
(Pill-beetle)

⑩
DERMESTIDAE
(Bacon-beetle)

⑧
CANTHARIDAE
(Soldier-beetle)

PLATE 7. COLEOPTERA II

9. Antennae

    (*a*) elbowed and clubbed [*see* Plate 6 (7) and (8)];
        (head projects in front of the eyes as a "beak"
        which *may* be very long) . . .
                FAMILY *CURCULIONIDAE* (p. 55)
    (*b*) of various shapes; (if they are elbowed and
        clubbed then there is no long "beak") . . 10 .

10. Colour

    (*a*) a combination of red, yellow or black spots;
        (rounded wing-cases) [*see* Plate 8 (6)] . .
                FAMILY *COCCINELLIDAE* (p. 48)
    (*b*) not as above. . . . . . 11.

11. Thorax

    (*a*) extending forwards as a "hood" masking most
        of the head. Examine [*see* Plate 6 (5)] very
        carefully . FAMILY *ANOBIIDAE* (p. 5)
    (*b*) not having this form 12

12. Antennae

    (*a*) resembling either Plate 7 (2) or Plate 7 (3) . 13
    (*b*) quite unlike either of the above . . . 14

13. Antennae

    (*a*) ending in a club consisting of several plates [*see*
        Plate 7 (2)]; general appearance of insect as in
        Plate 7 (1) or (4) . . . . .
                FAMILY *SCARABAEIDAE* (p. 53)
    (*b*) resembling [*see* Plate 7 (3)] . . . .
                FAMILY *LUCANIDAE* (p. 52)

14. Antennae

    (*a*) ending in a club 15
    (*b*) not ending in a club 23

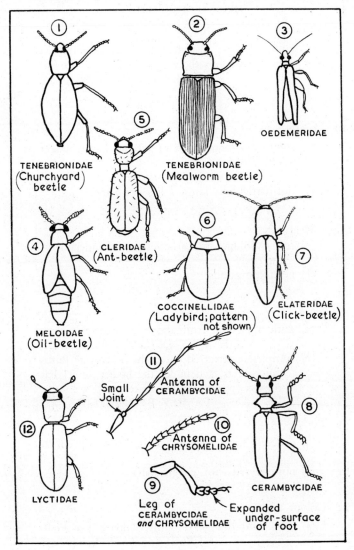

PLATE 8. COLEOPTERA III

15. Antennae

    (*a*) elbowed; (the last two segments of the abdomen
        not covered by the wing-cases) [*see* Plate 6 (6)]
                FAMILY *HISTERIDAE* (p. 49)

    (*b*) not elbowed.   16

16. Mouth-parts

    (*a*) some very long; (club of antenna hairy; insect
        often found in dung) .   .   .   .   .
             FAMILY *HYDROPHILIDAE* (p. 48)

    (*b*) not particularly long; (club not hairy)   .   .   17

17. Legs

    (*a*) readily folding into grooves on the underside of
        the body   18

    (*b*) not folding thus   19

18. Head

    (*a*) distinctly visible from above [*see* Plate 7 (10)]   .
            FAMILY *DERMESTIDAE* (p. 49)

    (*b*) completely retracted under the body; (*all* limbs
        can be retracted under the body; insect has
        convex appearance) [*see* Plate 7 (9)]   .   .
            FAMILY *BYRRHIDAE* (p. 48)

19. Body

    (*a*) covered with upright hairs (examine specimen
        from the side)   20

    (*b*) not covered with upright hairs   .   .   21

20. Colour

    (*a*) black and orange or entirely black [*see* Plate
        7 (6)]   .   FAMILY *SILPHIDAE* (p. 49)

    (*b*) not as described above .   .   .   .
            FAMILY *CLERIDAE* (p. 50)

21. Wing-cases
    (a) long and parallel sided [*see* Plate 8 (12)]; (insect
        in or near timber)
                FAMILY *LYCTIDAE* (p. 51)
    (b) not as shown in Plate 8 (12)   22

22. Feet
    (a) fore and middle-feet consisting of five joints,
        hind-feet of four joints; (black insect) . .
            FAMILY *TENEBRIONIDAE* (p. 51)
    (b) all feet consisting of four joints; (insect often
        with metallic sheen and end of abdomen not
        covered by wing-cases) . . . .
            FAMILY *NITIDULIDAE* (p. 49)

23. Abdomen
    (a) only slightly covered by the wing-cases [*see*
        Plate 7 (5) and Plate 8 (4)]   24
    (b) almost or completely covered . . .   25

24. General appearance
    (a) as in Plate 7 (5) *or* very small . . .
           FAMILY *STAPHYLINIDAE* (p. 49)
    (b) as in Plate 8 (4); (four joints in the hind-foot)
            FAMILY *MELOIDAE* (p. 52)

25. Body and wing-cases
    (a) soft   26
    (b) not soft   30

26. Feet
    (a) five joints in *all* the feet. . . .   27
    (b) fore and middle-foot consisting of five joints,
        hind-foot of four joints   29

27. Colour
    (a) green and red . . . .
           FAMILY *MALACHIIDAE* (p. 50)
    (b) shades of brown   28

28. Wing-cases

    (*a*) square cut at the end, not covering the abdomen
       [*see* Plate 7 (8)] .   .   .   .   .
               FAMILY *CANTHARIDAE* (p. 50)
    (*b*) tapering to a point at the end, covering the
       abdomen . FAMILY *DASCILLIDAE* (p. 51)

29. Head and thorax

    (*a*) very hairy .   FAMILY *LAGRIIDAE* (p. 52)
    (*b*) not hairy [*see* Plate 8 (3)] .   .   .
              FAMILY *OEDEMERIDAE* (p. 52)

30. Feet

    (*a*) *all* having four joints, under surface of the joints
       being broad [*see* Plate 8 (9)].   .   .   31
    (*b*) not *all* having four joints, under surface of the
       joints not broad.   32

31. Colour

    (*a*) often dull; (body long; antennae consisting of
       long joints) [*see* Plate 8 (8) and (11)] .   .
               FAMILY *CERAMBYCIDAE* (p. 53)
    (*b*) often a metallic sheen; (body usually rounded;
       antennae consisting of many small joints) [*see*
       Plate 8 (10)] .   .   .   .   .
              FAMILY *CHRYSOMELIDAE* (p. 54)

32. Feet

    (*a*) fore and middle-feet consisting of five joints,
       hind-foot of four joints, [*see* Plate 8 (1) and (2)]
          FAMILY *TENEBRIONIDAE* (p. 51)
    (*b*) number of joints not as above   .   .   33

33. Wing-cases

    (*a*) broad and usually black [*see* Plate 7 (7)] .   .
             FAMILY *SILPHIDAE* (p. 49)
    (*b*) not broad   34

34. Shape

    (*a*) long beetles of streamlined appearance, the thorax being closely fitted to the after body; (five joints in all the feet) [*see* Plate 8 (7)] .

                FAMILY *ELATERIDAE* (p. 51)

    (*b*) not streamlined; (colour blue or black, white and red) [*see* Plate 8 (5)] . . . .

                FAMILY *CLERIDAE* (p. 50)

NOTES ON THE FAMILIES OF COLEOPTERA

FAMILY *CICINDELIDAE*. Tiger beetles. Very active, fast runners and fliers. They are carnivorous, note the huge jaws. They frequent heaths and other sandy places. The commonest species is *Cicindela campestris*, 14 mm, emerald green wing cases each bearing five yellow spots.

    FAMILY *CARABIDAE*. A very large family of active beetles living on the ground, often under stones. Most are carnivorous. They have five joints in all the feet, and may thus be distinguished from some members of the Tenebrionidae which resemble them in general appearance and habits but have only four joints in the hind-foot. They are so numerous and similar that further division of the family is beyond the scope of this book.

    FAMILY *DYTISCIDAE*. These beetles are well suited to living in water—note their streamlined shape and paddle-like legs. They are fast swimmers and carnivorous. They are also strong fliers and so may be found in ponds everywhere. *Dytiscus marginalis*, the great water beetle, about 35 mm, wing cases almost smooth in the male and deeply furrowed in the female. The fore-legs of the male bear large pads which help in gripping the female during mating; this feature occurs in many members of the family.

    FAMILY *HYGROBIIDAE*. One species only. *Hygrobia hermanni*, very common near the bottom of ponds; 9 mm, wing cases brown with central black markings. It is known as the screech beetle because of the sound it produces by rubbing the tip of the abdomen against the wing cases.

FAMILY *GYRINIDAE*. Whirligig beetles. The antennae and hind two pairs of legs are short, thus avoiding confusion with the Dytiscidae (above). Note the eyes—they are divided into an upper portion for seeing above the water when the insect skims along the surface, and a lower portion for seeing under water.

FAMILY *HYDROPHILIDAE*. The characteristic feature is the long mouth-parts, which a casual observer might confuse with the shorter antennae. This character serves to distinguish them from the Dytiscidae (above) which have long antennae. Some are water beetles and others live in dung. *Hydrophilus piceus* [*see* Plate 6 (3)], the largest British water beetle, about 40 mm. It swims less quickly than *Dytiscus marginalis* (above) and also differs from it in being herbivorous. The genera which live in dung are much smaller and more rounded than *Hydrophilus*.

FAMILY *COCCINELLIDAE*. Ladybirds. These beetles have strongly convex wing cases, usually in bright colours spotted with black. They are carnivorous, feeding actively on green-fly (Hemiptera, Aphididae, p. 30) and are one of the important natural controls on this pest. The following species are all very common. *Adalia bipunctata*, two-spot ladybird, 5 mm, red with a black spot on each wing case. There are, however, several other colour forms of this species. *Coccinella septempunctata*, seven-spot ladybird, 7 mm, red with three distinct black spots on each wing case and a seventh spot where two smaller ones meet on the closed wing cases. *Coccinella decempunctata*, ten-spot ladybird, 5 to 8 mm, red with ten black spots. *Thea vigintiduopunctata*, twenty-two-spot ladybird, 4 mm, very pale yellow with minute black spots. *Propylea quatuor-decimguttata*, fourteen-spot ladybird, 4 to 5 mm, pale yellow with most of the black in the form of short stripes rather than dots.

FAMILY *BYRRHIDAE*. Pill beetles. The head and legs are retracted under the body when the insect is disturbed. The commonest species is *Byrrhus pilula*, 6 or 7 mm, brownish [*see* Plate 7 (9)]. Found on the ground, especially in sandy places.

FAMILY *DERMESTIDAE*. Many are of economic importance, feeding on hides and other stored goods, but others are found out of doors on flowers. *Dermestes lardarius* [*see* Plate 7 (10)], the bacon beetle, 7 to 9 mm, blackish, front half of wing-cases buff with dark spots. Other species of *Dermestes* feed on dried insects in collections.

FAMILY *NITIDULIDAE*. Very common on decaying animal and vegetable matter and on almost all flowers. The clubbed antennae make them easy to spot. There are a great many species.

FAMILY *STAPHYLINIDAE*. Devil's coach horses. They are very numerous and easily spotted. They move in a scurrying manner, waving the abdomen from side to side and, when disturbed, raising it up and curling it forwards like a scorpion's tail. They are often caught in flight, and because of their size and the almost imperceptible wing-cases are easily mistaken for small flies (Diptera). The larger ones are black and have the same general appearance as our largest species, *Staphylinus olens* [*see* Plate 7 (5)] 25 mm, but many of the smaller ones have more pointed abdomens and may be brightly coloured in red or green. They are not of economic importance; they feed on small particles and organisms and are found in most situations, often under stones, and many of the smaller ones on flowers and carrion.

FAMILY *HISTERIDAE*. Round bodied shiny beetles which retract their legs and sham death when disturbed. The last two segments of the abdomen are not hidden by the wing cases. Usually found in decaying matter. *Hister unicolor* [*see* Plate 6 (6)], 8 mm, black, large jaws and strong broad shanks.

FAMILY *SILPHIDAE*. Carrion beetles and burying beetles. Most are to be found near dead animals on which they feed. The burying, or sexton, beetles dig soil from under small animals thus burying them quite swiftly. They then lay their eggs near them. The commonest burying beetle is *Necrophorus investigator* in which the club of the antennae is orange and the wing-cases black with orange stripes extending right across them. *Necrophorus vespillo* [*see* Plate 7 (6)] resembles it, but the shank of the hind-leg is curved.

Key to the Commoner Species of Carrion Beetles

1. Colour
   - (a) thorax red . . . *Oeceoptoma thoracica*
   - (b) thorax not red 2

2. Jaws
   - (a) very long and projecting 3
   - (b) not very long 4

3. Wing-cases
   - (a) quite smooth . . . *Ablattaria laevigata*
   - (b) furrowed lengthways . . *Phosphuga atrata*

4. Where found
   - (a) in carrion . . . *Thanatophilus rugosus*
   - (b) not in carrion [*see* Plate 7 (7)], (wing-cases slightly furrowed) . . . . *Silpha tristis*

FAMILY *CANTHARIDAE*. Soldier beetles. The long antennae and legs, soft wing-cases and rather slow flight make them familiar objects on any sunny day throughout the summer. They occur in large numbers on showy flowers, particularly Umbelliferae. There are several species, not easy to tell apart. The glow worm belongs to this family, the female has no wings or wing-cases and is best recognized by its glow which is produced near the end of the underside of the abdomen.

FAMILY *MALACHIIDAE*. Closely related to the Cantharidae (above). *Malachius bipustulatus*, our commonest species, 5 to 7 mm, bright green with red tips to the wing-cases.

FAMILY *CLERIDAE*. These beetles have rather flattened bodies and are clad with erect hairs which are very noticeable if the specimen is viewed from the side. *Thanasimus formicarius*, the ant beetle, 9 mm, thorax red, wing-cases black and white. The arrangement of the colours is such as to give the impression of a thin ant-like waist. It is very active and is found under bark where it feeds on other wood-inhabiting insects. *Korynetes coeruleus*, 5 mm, bright blue all over. Under the bark of trees. *Necrobia ruficollis*, 5 mm, differs from the two above species in having clubbed antennae, thorax red, wing-cases bluish green. On carrion.

FAMILY *DASCILLIDAE*. One species only. *Dascillus cervinus*, 11 mm, buff colour all over, long antennae. Rather sluggish, found on flowers and bushes.

FAMILY *ANOBIIDAE*. Furniture beetles. The "hood" formed by the thorax partly covering the head provides a useful spot feature. *Xestobium rufovillosum*, the death watch beetle is 6 to 9 mm, brownish. *Anobium*, about 3 mm, dark brown.

FAMILY *LYCTIDAE*. Powder post beetles. Species of *Lyctus*, about 5 mm, parallel sided and flattened. They live in wood.

FAMILY *ELATERIDAE*. Click beetles. A family of great economic importance. The larvae of some species are the wire-worm pests of root crops and live in the ground, but other adults and larvae live in wood. When the adult falls on its back it can right itself by bringing the thorax and abdomen together sharply, thus producing an undirected leap accompanied by the characteristic click. The following is a rough guide to a few of the commoner species. *Athous haemorrhoidalis*, 8 to 13 mm, thorax black, wing-cases reddish brown. Very common on foliage. *Athous bicolor*, 8 to 11 mm, thorax black, wing-cases buff. On foliage. *Dalopius marginatus*, 6 mm, thorax black with reddish margin, wing-cases buff with black stripe along the inner margin of each. On foliage. *Prosternon tessellatum*, 10 mm, thorax and wing-cases black and covered with light yellow hairs forming circular patterns. On foliage. *Limonius minutus*, 5.5 to 7 mm, entirely jet black. On foliage. *Melanotus rufipes*, 12 to 18 mm, black with red legs. In rotten wood or on foliage. *Agriotes*. This genus is perhaps the most important economically. It can be spotted by examining the antennae; the second joint being as long as the fourth, whereas in other genera it is much shorter. In general appearance the species of *Agriotes* resemble those of *Athous*. *Agriotes obscurus* is 8 or 9 mm, a very serious pest.

FAMILY *TENEBRIONIDAE*. A large family. The predominant colour is black, and form and habits vary considerably. Some bear an outward resemblance to the Carabidae family (p. 47) but they can be distinguished by having only four joints in the hind-foot instead of five. This feature relates the Tenebrionidae to the next three families described below. *Tenebrio molitor* [*see* Plate 8 (2)], 15 mm, a common pest of stored flour, the damage being caused by its larva, the mealworm. *Tribolium*, 3 to 4 mm, resembles Tenebrio but has clubbed antennae. It has similar habits. *Blaps mucronata* [*see* Plate 8 (1)], 21 mm, one of the species which resemble the Carabidae. It does not fly, the wing-cases cannot open. It lives in cellars.

FAMILY *OEDEMERIDAE.* Related to the Tenebrionidae (above). The appearance of the wing-cases is characteristic, they seem too narrow to cover the abdomen completely. Species of *Oedemera* are very common throughout the summer on flowers, especially Compositae, on whose pollen they feed. Many species are of greenish colour.

FAMILY *LAGRIIDAE.* Related to the Tenebrionidae (above). Only one species occurs in Britain. *Lagria hirta*, 9 to 10 mm, head and thorax black, wing-cases buff, whole body hairy. Quite common on bushes in the summer.

FAMILY *MELOIDAE.* Oil beetles. Related to the three preceding families by the number of joints in the feet. *Meloe proscarabaeus* [*see* Plate 8 (4)], 23 mm. The life history is remarkable. The female lays thousands of eggs, and the larvae attach themselves to solitary bees which carry them to their own burrows. The larval stages are completed in the burrows, and the adult insects emerge in spring. There are other smaller species of *Meloe*. *Apalus muralis*, 10 mm, wing-cases slender and yellowish. Its development resembles that of *Meloe*.

FAMILY *LUCANIDAE.* All three British species lay their eggs in the wood of decaying deciduous trees. The larval stages may last for several years. *Lucanus cervus*, the stag beetle, over 38 mm, in the male and over 34 mm in the female. The males have long jaws which may be as much as one third of the total length of the beetle. They are the largest British beetles. *Dorcus parallelipipedus*, the little stag, 25 mm, jaws larger in the male than in the female but never very large. *Sinodendron cylindricum*, 13 mm, body tubular instead of flattened, a horn projects from the middle of the head in the male.

Note. The Lucanidae are not *very* common, though they are usually plentiful where they occur. They should not be destroyed indiscriminately as they are quite harmless both to man and to trees, living, as they do, in wood which has already begun to decay.

FAMILY *SCARABAEIDAE*. Chafers and dung beetles. This large family consists of two distinct groups, the chafers which are often pests, and the dung beetles which are beneficial to agriculture. The dung beetles in general have the rounded shape of Plate 7 (4) and are often blackish in colour, whereas the chafers [*see* Plate 7 (1)] are not rounded and are often brownish in colour. The legs of dung beetles are strong and suited to digging. The larvae of chafers are known as white-grubs; they live in the ground and feed on the roots of herbs and of trees. The adults are often found on foliage and fly mostly at night. The following is a guide to some of the larger chafers. *Cetonia aurata*, the rose chafer, 18 mm, bright green. Not common and not a pest. *Melolontha melolontha*, the cockchafer [*see* Plate 7 (1)], one of the largest British insects, over 25 mm, wing-cases brown, common. *Amphimallon solstitialis*, the mid-summer chafer, 16 mm, wing-cases brown, body hairy. *Serica brunnea*, the brown chafer, about 10 mm, entirely light brown, plates of antennae very large, body not hairy. *Phyllopertha horticola*, the garden chafer, about 8 mm, thorax blue-black, wing-cases straw coloured. Very abundant in some years.

All the dung beetles lay their eggs in or near dung, and feed on it. In the course of their egg-laying they excavate the ground under large cow pats, etc., thereby burying them and so fertilizing the ground. We have over sixty species; the following are among the most often seen. *Geotrupes stercorarius*, about 22 mm, dull black on whole of upper surface and metallic blue beneath. *Geotrupes vernalis* [*see* Plate 7 (4)], about 16 mm, glossy black upper surface and violet under surface.

FAMILY *CERAMBYCIDAE*. Longhorn beetles. Members of this family bear a superficial resemblance to the Cantharidae (p. 50), but may be distinguished by having hard wing-cases and four joints in the feet instead of five. They are related to the Chrysomelidae (p. 54), and share with them an exclusively vegetarian diet. Some of the more slender members of the Chrysomelidae may be confused with them, but examination of the antennae and comparison of Plate 8 (10) and Plate 8 (11) will verify the identification. Many Cerambycidae are of economic importance; all lay eggs in wood though the adults may also be found on flowers. None of the common species described here is a pest. *Rhagium bifasciatum* [*see* Plate 8 (8)], about 17 mm, glossy black with yellow hairs scattered over the body and two sloping dull yellow bands across the wing-cases. In pine woods, in or on decaying stumps. *Clytus arietis*, the wasp beetle, 7 to 14 mm, black with three bright yellow marks on each wing-case, thighs dark, shanks and feet light brown. Often found on trunks of apple trees, moving its antennae and abdomen in a manner very suggestive of a wasp. *Grammoptera ruficornis*, 5 mm, black except for some light brown on the antennae, fore-legs and the base of the shanks of the middle and hind-legs. *Tetrops praeusta*, 4 mm, head, antennae and thorax black, wing-cases buff, densely clad with hairs. On gorse and hawthorn flowers.

FAMILY *CHRYSOMELIDAE*. A very large family containing many species of great economic importance. Most have rounded bodies but a few are elongated. *Timarcha tenebricosa*, the bloody nosed beetle, 23 mm, the largest member of the family, entirely black. It is slow moving and when disturbed secretes a red fluid from its mouth, whence its name. Leaf beetles. Many species are found on flowers; they are usually slow moving and of brilliant metallic coloration. Flea beetles. Very active and can jump well. The thighs of the hind-legs are large in order to accommodate the jumping muscles. Their larvae are serious pests of the cabbage family, the Cruciferae, and especially of the turnip, whose leaves they eat with great speed. *Cassida viridis*, the mint tortoise beetle, 6 to 7 mm, the large shield-like thorax completely covers the head. Its larva feeds on mint leaves.

Of the species which are not rounded, but elongated, the majority live close to water. *Donacia*, there are several species, some very small. A common one is over 10 mm; the males are to be found near water and the females actually in the water, the larvae feeding on water plants. *Crioceris asparagi*, the asparagus beetle, 4 to 6 mm, head black, thorax red, wing-cases mottled blue and cream. An agricultural pest.

FAMILY *CURCULIONIDAE.* Weevils. The largest single family in the animal kingdom. It is of the utmost economic importance. There is great uniformity of appearance within the family which may be recognized by the shape of the antennae and, in the living beetle, by the characteristic stance. They are so numerous that they have taken to all modes of life, and there is scarcely any crop or stored product that is not attacked by some species of weevil. In general the female bores into the grain or other food by means of the mouth-parts which are often (but by no means always) at the end of a long snout, and then lays its eggs in the hole. It is the feeding larvae which to the damage. Any attempt at describing species is quite beyond the scope of this book.

FAMILY *SCOLYTIDAE.* Bark beetles. Of great economic importance. They make tunnels in the wood of ash, elm, pine etc., just under the bark. The body is compactly built, very hairy and with few prominent features, so that the identification of species is best accomplished by examining the shape of their tunnels.

ORDER **HYMENOPTERA**

THE members of this order are characterized by having two pairs of almost transparent wings, the hind-wing being much smaller than the fore-wing. A confirmatory feature may be sought in the method of coupling between the two wings. The hind edge of the fore-wing is folded under, and a row of hooks on the front edge of the hind-wing catches in the fold. Although the hooks are very small their presence may be demonstrated by bringing the hind-wing up to the fore-wing, from below, when it will be found to adhere to it.

Hymenoptera are remarkable among insects for their advanced social behaviour. Many species live in colonies whose various members perform definite tasks; the function of queens (females) and drones (males) is to reproduce the species, while workers attend to the daily work of the colony—nest building, food gathering etc. The social habit is not equally developed among all Hymenoptera; it is greatest in the hive bees and the ants, less perfect in the humble-bees and true wasps (Vespidae) and either absent or only slightly manifested in the other families.

The Hymenoptera are divided into two Sub-orders—

Thorax and abdomen of same width throughout
SUB-ORDER **CHALASTOGASTRA**

Thorax and abdomen separated by a narrow "waist." (If the insect is so hairy that the feature is difficult to see, it belongs to this group)
SUB-ORDER **CLISTOGASTRA**

KEY TO THE FAMILIES OF CHALASTOGASTRA
1. Shank of fore-leg
    (*a*) with two spurs at the end [*see* Plate 9 (1)] .   .
              FAMILY *TENTHREDINIDAE* (p. 64)
    (*b*) with only one spur at the end[1]   2

[1] A spur is a distinct large pointed structure, not to be confused with other small projections which may be present.

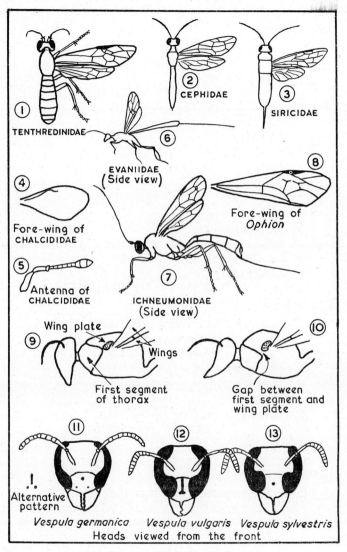

PLATE 9. HYMENOPTERA I

Figs. 9 and 10 are shown from the left-hand side

2. Abdomen

    (*a*) massive, almost parallel sided [*see* Plate 9 (3)]   .
                    FAMILY *SIRICIDAE* (p. 64)

    (*b*) slender [*see* Plate 9 (2)]   .   .   .   .
                    FAMILY *CEPHIDAE* (p. 64)

KEY TO THE FAMILIES OF CLISTOGASTRA

1. Wings

    (*a*) absent   2

    (*b*) present   3

2. Antennae

    (*a*) elbowed [*see* Plate 11 (1)]   .   .   .
                    FAMILY *FORMICIDAE* (p. 65)

    (*b*) not elbowed; (body covered in hairs); [*see*
        Plate 10 (3)]   .   .   .   .   .
                    FAMILY *MUTILLIDAE* (p. 67)

3. Wings

    (*a*) with scarcely any veins [*see* Plate 9 (4)]; very
        small insect; antennae as in Plate 9 (5)   .
                    FAMILY *CHALCIDIDAE* (p. 65)

    (*b*) with several veins   4

4. Antennae

    (*a*) elbowed [*see* Plate 11 (1)]   .   .   .
                    FAMILY *FORMICIDAE* (p. 65)

    (*b*) not as in Plate 11 (1)   5

5. Wing veins

    (*a*) similar to pattern shown in Plate 9 (6), (7) or
        (8)[1]   6

    (*b*) quite different from the patterns shown in the
        above figures   7

[1] Features characteristic of this group are the long slender waist and long antennae, and in the female, the very long egg-laying apparatus.

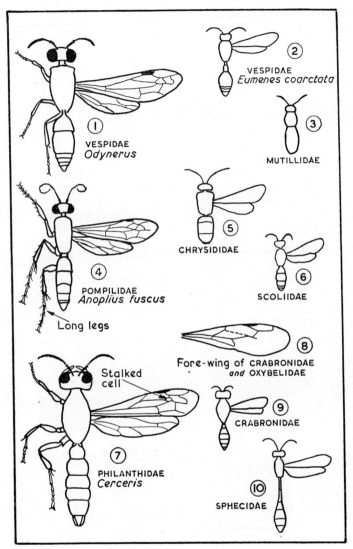

1. VESPIDAE *Odynerus*
2. VESPIDAE *Eumenes coarctata*
3. MUTILLIDAE
4. POMPILIDAE *Anoplius fuscus* — Long legs
5. CHRYSIDIDAE
6. SCOLIIDAE
7. PHILANTHIDAE *Cerceris* — Stalked cell
8. Fore-wing of CRABRONIDAE *and* OXYBELIDAE
9. CRABRONIDAE
10. SPHECIDAE

PLATE 10. HYMENOPTERA II

6. Abdomen

>   (*a*) joined to the upper part of the thorax [*see* Plate 8 (6)]   .   FAMILY *EVANIIDAE* (p. 65)
>   (*b*) joined to the lower part of the thorax [*see* Plate 9 (7)]   .   .   .   .   .   .
>   FAMILY *ICHNEUMONIDAE* (p. 65)

7. Thorax

>   (*a*) first segment reaches the wing-plate [*see* Plate 9 (9)][1], (examine the specimen from the side)
>   ("WASPS")   8
>   (*b*) first segment does not reach the wing-plate, [*see* Plate 9 (10)].   .   .   .   .   .
>   (**"BEES" and "SPHECOIDS"**)   12

8. Antennae

>   (*a*) thicker near the end than at the base [*see* Plate 9 (11), (12) and (13)]   .   .   .   .   .
>   FAMILY *VESPIDAE* (p. 66)
>   (*b*) not thicker near the end than at the base   .   .   9

9. Hind-legs

>   (*a*) long, projecting well beyond the end of the abdomen; (wings often cloudy); [*see* Plate 10 (4)]   .   FAMILY *POMPILIDAE* (p. 66)
>   (*b*) not particularly long   10

10. Body

>   (*a*) thickly covered with velvety hairs [*see* Plate 10 (3), but winged]   .   .   .   .   .
>   FAMILY *MUTILLIDAE* (p. 67)
>   (*b*) not thickly covered with velvety hairs   .   .   11

11. Coloration

>   (*a*) brilliant metallic, red and golden lustre [*see* Plate 10 (5)]   .   .   .   .   .
>   FAMILY *CHRYSIDIDAE* (p. 67)

---

[1] If the insect is so hairy that this feature cannot be seen at all, then it is a "BEE," refer to 19.

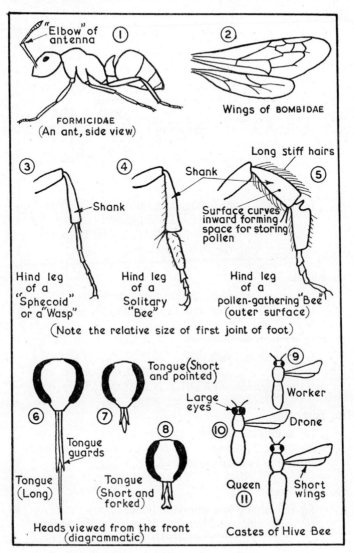

"Elbow" of antenna

① FORMICIDAE
(An ant, side view)

② Wings of BOMBIDAE

③ Shank

Hind leg
of a
"Sphecoid"
or a "Wasp"

④ Shank

Hind leg
of a
Solitary
"Bee"

⑤ Long stiff hairs

Surface curves
inward forming
space for storing
pollen

Hind leg
of a
pollen-gathering "Bee"
(outer surface)

(Note the relative size of first joint of foot)

⑥ Tongue guards

Tongue
(Long)

⑦ Tongue (Short
and pointed)

⑧ Tongue
(Short and
forked)

Heads viewed from the front
(diagrammatic)

⑨ Worker

Large
eyes

⑩ Drone

Queen
⑪

Short
wings

Castes of Hive Bee

PLATE 11. HYMENOPTERA III

   (*b*) not as above [*see* Plate 10 (6)] .   .   .   .
FAMILY SCOLIIDAE (p. 66)

12. Hind-foot

   (*a*) consisting of five roughly similar joints [*see* Plate 11 (3)]; (insect never very hairy) .   .
("SPHECOIDS")   13

   (*b*) the first joint is both much longer *and* thicker than the others [*see* Plate 11 (4) and (5)]; (insect often very hairy[1]) .   . ("BEES")   19

13. Insect

   (*a*) having a very long and thin waist [*see* Plate 10 (10)], buff and black coloration   .   .
FAMILY SPHECIDAE (p. 67)

   (*b*) not having the above appearance   .   .   14

14. Middle-legs

   (*a*) having two spurs at the end of the shank.   .   15

   (*b*) having only one spur at the end of the shank   .   16

15. First segment of abdomen

   (*a*) slender and stalk-like   .   .   .   .   .
FAMILY MELLINIDAE (p. 67)

   (*b*) not slender   . FAMILY NYSSONIDAE (p. 67)

16. Fore-wing

   (*a*) as in [Plate 10 (7)] .   .   .   .   .   .
FAMILY PHILANTHIDAE (p. 67)

   (*b*) not as in [Plate 10 (7)]   17

17. Fore-wing

   (*a*) resembling that shown in [Plate 10 (8)]   .   .   18

   (*b*) quite different from that shown in [Plate 10 (8)]
FAMILY PEMPHREDONIDAE (p. 68)

---

[1] The conclusive feature for inclusion among the Bees is the presence of some branched hairs on the body, but this feature can be seen only with the aid of a very strong lens.

18. Fore-wing [*see* Plate 10 (8)]

    (*a*) dotted line thickly veined . . . .
           FAMILY *CRABRONIDAE* (p. 68)
    (*b*) dotted line thinly veined . . . .
           FAMILY *OXYBELIDAE* (p. 68)

19. Hind-leg

    (*a*) having no spurs at the end of the shank . .
           FAMILY *APIDAE* (p. 68)
    (*b*) having spurs at the end of the shank . . 20

20. Abdomen

    (*a*) thickly clad with hairs 21
    (*b*) sparsely clad or hairless 25

21. Tongue

    (*a*) not long [*see* Plate 11 (7)] . . . .
           FAMILY *ANDRENIDAE* (p. 69)
    (*b*) long or very long [*see* Plate 11 (6)] . . . 22

22. Wing-veins

    (*a*) as in [Plate 11 (2)]; (very hairy body) . .
           FAMILY *BOMBIDAE* (p. 68)
    (*b*) not as in [Plate 11 (2)] 23

23. Abdomen

    (*a*) very thickly clad with *long* hairs . . .
           FAMILY *ANTHOPHORIDAE* (p. 69)
    (*b*) not clad thus; (head large and round) . . 24

24. Head

    (*a*) large and round . . . . . .
           FAMILY *MEGACHILIDAE* (p. 69)
    (*b*) not particularly large . . . . .
           FAMILY *NOMADIDAE* (p. 69)

25. Tongue

    (*a*) long [*see* Plate 11 (6)] 26
    (*b*) short [*see* Plate 11 (7) or (8)] 27

26. Appearance

    (*a*) hairy, large round head . . . . .
                FAMILY *MEGACHILIDAE* (p. 69)
    (*b*) almost hairless, wasp-like or black . . .
                FAMILY *NOMADIDAE* (p. 69)

27. Body

    (*a*) almost or entirely without hairs; (small black
        bees) . FAMILY *PROSOPIDAE* (p. 69)
    (*b*) distinctly hairy 28

28. Tongue

    (*a*) forked at the tip [*see* Plate 11 (8)] . . .
                FAMILY *COLLETIDAE* (p. 69)
    (*b*) pointed at the tip [*see* Plate 11(7)] . . .
                FAMILY *ANDRENIDAE* (p. 69)

NOTES ON THE FAMILIES OF HYMENOPTERA

FAMILY *SIRICIDAE*. Wood wasps or horntails. Two species are found in Britain but they are not of great economic importance here. The female lays her eggs, one at a time, deep in the wood of conifers by means of her long and powerful egg-laying organ. The larvae, on hatching, cause damage by burrowing deeper into the wood. *Urocerus gigas* [*see* Plate 9 (3)], very large, coloured yellow and black. Its larvae are attacked in the wood by the large ichneumon *Rhyssa persuasoria* (p. 65) which seeks them out and lays a few eggs on each. *Sirex cyaneus*, smaller, blue.

FAMILY *CEPHIDAE*. Stem saw-flies. Slender bodied. The eggs are laid in the stems of grasses (and consequently of cereal crops), and of reeds. Only a few species occur in Britain and they are not very serious pests.

FAMILY *TENTHREDINIDAE*. Saw-flies. A large family of great economic importance. The females' egg-laying organ is in the form of a saw, and by means of this the eggs are laid in the leaves of many trees, shrubs and herbs. The larvae feed on the leaves, thereby damaging the plant and the formation of its fruit. Most cultivated fruit trees and shrubs are attacked by some species of saw-fly.

FAMILY *CHALCIDIDAE*. A very important family whose members are so small that they are not often observed, or else put down as "small flies." They lay their eggs in caterpillars and are therefore responsible for keeping down the numbers of many plant pests. They are very numerous, both in individuals and in species.

FAMILY *EVANIIDAE*. Closely related to the Ichneumonidae. They are easily spotted in flight by the way in which the abdomen is held above the thorax on its slender waist.

FAMILY *ICHNEUMONIDAE*[1]. A very important family. It is not possible to give any single easy feature by which they may be recognized, but the family usually combines a certain type of wing venation, a long slender "waist" and a delicate abdomen. They lay their eggs chiefly in the caterpillars of Lepidoptera. A long egg-laying apparatus is almost always present in the female, and by means of it the caterpillar is stabbed and paralysed prior to the insertion of the eggs. The ichneumon larva feeds on the caterpillar. Ichneumons kill so many caterpillars in this way that they are valuable in keeping down the numbers of plant pests. The caterpillars of the cabbage white butterfly are attacked by more than one species of ichneumon. *Rhyssa persuasoria*, male 23 mm, female 30 mm not including the egg-laying organ, is our largest ichneumon. It occurs in woodlands, where it lays eggs on the larva of *Urocerus gigas* (p. 64) which it reaches by thrusting its egg-laying organ through solid wood. *Ophion luteus*, male 15 mm, female 20 mm, fore-wing [*see* Plate 9 (8)], light buff colour, abdomen flattened sideways, egg-laying apparatus very short.

FAMILY *FORMICIDAE*. Ants. A very large family though there are only thirty species in Britain, where they are rarely of economic importance. The social habit is highly developed, and ant colonies are permanent, i.e. they are not started afresh each spring as are those of wasps and humble bees. Only the males

---

[1] The Ichneumonidae are here taken to include the Family BRACONIDAE which is closely related and differs from the Ichneumonidae in a small feature of the wings.

and females have wings, and they may be seen in large numbers during the pairing season at the height of the summer. When the pairing flight is over, the males die and the surviving females shed their wings before either founding new colonies or re-entering their parent colony.

FAMILY *VESPIDAE*. To this family belong the insects which we generally recognize as "wasps" round the jam jars. They are social wasps, and make nests of wood pulp chewed with their jaws. They are both carnivorous and vegetarian, and may be found in large numbers near fruit trees, feeding on the fruit both on the tree and on the ground. The castes can be distinguished by the number of joints in the antennae—12 in the queens and workers, 13 in the males. The workers are much smaller than either of the others. The commoner species can be identified by means of the markings on the face [*see* Plate 9 (11), (12) and (13)]. *Vespa crabro*, the hornet, is at least 20 mm and the markings on the body are tawny rather than yellow.

The family also includes some solitary wasps. *Odynerus*, the mason wasps [*see* Plate 10 (1)]. They can be distinguished from the social wasps by the more obvious "waist" and by the more glossy abdomen. The female makes a burrow on the sunny side of a bank or of an old wall, and having laid its eggs, fills the burrow with paralysed caterpillars on which its larvae feed when they hatch. There are several species. *Eumenes coarctata*, the potter wasp [*see* Plate 10 (2)]. It can be identified at once by means of the slender first segment of the abdomen. The female makes a little nest of clay and saliva round the stem of low-growing plants and stocks it in much the same way as does *Odynerus*.

FAMILY *SCOLIIDAE*. A large family in hot countries; there are two British species. *Tiphia femorata* [*see* Plate 10 (6)], 10 mm, black with flattened thighs.

FAMILY *POMPILIDAE*. Spider-hunting wasps. The female paralyses spiders and drags them to her nest which is a hole in the ground. She then lays an egg on them, and the larva feeds on the spiders which, having been paralysed but not killed, remain fresh. In the field these wasps attract attention by their swift running movements as they drag the spiders towards their nests. A spider may be paralysed many feet from the nest and as the wasp drags it only a few inches at a time the journey may take several hours. *Anoplius fuscus* [*see* Plate 10 (4)], our largest species, 12 mm, black with red on the abdomen. It preys on the wolf spider *Trochosa terricola* (p. 102).

FAMILY *CHRYSIDIDAE*. Ruby tailed wasps. A small family which can be spotted by the nature of the abdomen which is hard and consists of only three apparent segments on its upper surface. They lay their eggs in the nests of other solitary wasps and solitary bees.

FAMILY *MUTILLIDAE*. Velvet "ants." A small family. *Mutilla europea* [*see* Plate 10 (3)], 15 mm, the female is wingless, red and black with white stripes on the abdomen, the sting is painful. The eggs are laid in the nests of humble bees, the larvae feeding on the bee larvae. The males are not often seen.

FAMILY *SPHECIDAE*. Sand wasps. The female digs a deep burrow in sandy soil and provisions it with a caterpillar near which it lays its egg, and then seals up the entrance. The wasp larva feeds on the caterpillar which is often much larger than the parent wasp. There is only one genus, *Ammophila*.

FAMILY *MELLINIDAE*. The first segment of the abdomen is very narrow causing the waist to be prolonged as a "stalk." They burrow in sandy soil and provision the burrow with Diptera. One genus only, *Mellinus*.

FAMILY *NYSSONIDAE*. The species of *Gorytes* provision their nests with young frog hoppers which they seize in spite of their foamy covering (p. 29). Species of *Nysson* do not make burrows of their own but lay their eggs in those made by *Gorytes*. *Nysson*, the veins of the fore-wing resemble those in Plate 10 (7)—note the small stalked cell—*Gorytes*, the fore-wing is without the small stalked cell.

FAMILY *PHILANTHIDAE*. These are wasps with shining yellow and black abdomens and long curved jaws. The females make burrows in sandy ground and provision them with beetles (one species takes solitary bees) on which the larvae feed. *Cerceris*, the only genus in Britain, may be recognized at once by its wing venation [*see* Plate 10 (7)]—note especially the "stalk" arising from the small cell in the fore-wing. There are four common species.

FAMILY *PEMPHREDONIDAE*. A family of many small black wasps.

FAMILY *CRABRONIDAE*. A very large family. The head is broad and the jaws large. The first segment of the abdomen is slender, giving almost the appearance of a stalk. Many are entirely black. There is one genus only, *Crabro* [see Plate 10 (9)].

FAMILY *OXYBELIDAE*. Very small wasps. They provision their burrows with small Diptera.

FAMILY *APIDAE*. We have one species only, *Apis mellifera*, the hive bee. Because of the part which they play in pollinating flowers they are among the most important of all insects, both in nature and, consequently, to human economy. In these bees the social habit is seen in a very advanced form. All members of the hive have their particular tasks. The workers are the only ones which gather food, nectar and pollen, which, on returning to the hive, they make into honey for feeding to the larvae. There is only one queen to each nest. Most of the eggs which she lays become worker bees, but a few become queens and males (drones). When the population of the hive reaches a certain size the queen and some of the workers leave it to found a new colony elsewhere (swarming)—while one of the new queens takes over the hive. She is fertilized by one of the drones during a pairing flight after which she returns to the hive. The colonies thus survive from year to year. The castes differ in appearance as illustrated in Plate 11 (9), (10) and (11).

FAMILY *BOMBIDAE*. Humble (or bumble) bee. They are easily recognized by their furry appearance and by the way in which the abdomen seems to be held curled under the body. There are queens, males and workers, but the social habit is much less developed than in the hive bee (above). The queens come out of hibernation in the spring and start making a nest in the soil and lay a few eggs which all develop into workers. These then enlarge the nest. Later, queens and drones (as well as more workers) hatch out, and pair in flight. The old colonies, drones and workers, all die out in the autumn, only the new queens surviving the winter. There are two genera only. *Bombus*, the true humble bees. The shank of the hind-leg is constructed to form a pollen collecting organ [*see* Plate 11 (5)]. There are fifteen British species. *Psithyrus*, cuckoo bees. These bees have no pollen collecting organ. They lay their eggs in the nests of *Bombus* after killing the queen, and their larvae are fed by the *Bombus* workers.

The species of Bombidae may be identified by means of their colour patterns—*see* the book list.

FAMILY *MEGACHILIDAE*. This family includes bees of various burrowing habits, some excavating in the ground or in rotten wood, others in plant stems. A distinguishing feature is the large head, which, in many cases, is little smaller than the thorax. The jaws, too, are large.

FAMILY *ANTHOPHORIDAE*. Bees resembling small humble bees. They make nests in the ground. Genus *Anthophora*.

FAMILY *ANDRENIDAE*. A large family of rather hairy bees. They make deep burrows in which the eggs are laid on a supply of honey which serves as food for the larvae. There are several genera.

FAMILY *COLLETIDAE*. It is difficult to give any simple feature for separating these bees from the Andrenidae (above) which they resemble not only in superficial appearance but also in habits. The split tongue is an absolutely reliable feature, and can be stretched out for examination in a newly killed specimen. There is one genus only, *Colletes*.

FAMILY *PROSOPIDAE*. Small, black and almost hairless bees. One genus, *Prosopis*.

FAMILY *NOMADIDAE*. Superficially most members of this family resemble wasps rather than bees, having no hairs on the abdomen which is shiny and striped in black (or brown) and yellow. They lay their eggs in the nests of other solitary bees. *Nomada*, abdomen hairless and wasp-like. *Melecta*, abdomen hairy, black and white.

ORDER **DIPTERA**

(True Flies)

THIS is one of the largest orders both in numbers of species and of individuals. There are over 5,000 British species. Flies have only one pair of wings, while the other (hind) pair is present in the form of small organs concerned with maintaining balance in flight. These are the halteres [*see* Plate 12 (6)] and must not be confused with basal lobes which are part of the true wings of some flies [*see* Plate 12 (10), (11) and (12)]. Diptera are of various habits and have mouth-parts of several kinds, but never of the biting type as in the Orthoptera. It is not an easy order to classify, and the student may have difficulty in deciding to which sub-order his specimen belongs.

The Diptera may first be divided into three Sub-orders. Read and compare the following features very carefully—

Antennae slender and consisting of many joints, prominent (except in Bibionidae [*see* Plate 12 (1)]); abdomen long and slender (except Bibionidae)
SUB-ORDER **NEMATOCERA**

Antennae consisting of three joints (never more than six) [*see* Plate 12 (3) and (4)]; abdomen often long, never very short ### SUB-ORDER **BRACHYCERA**

Antennae generally *appearing* to consist of one joint and a projecting thread [*see* Plate 12 (8)]; abdomen often short as in House fly [*see* Plate 12 (9)]
SUB-ORDER **CYCLORRHAPHA**

KEY TO THE FAMILIES OF NEMATOCERA

1. Legs
   - (*a*) long slender and easy to break; (insect usually over 12 mm) FAMILY *TIPULIDAE* (p. 74.)
   - (*b*) not very long and not very easily broken .   .   2

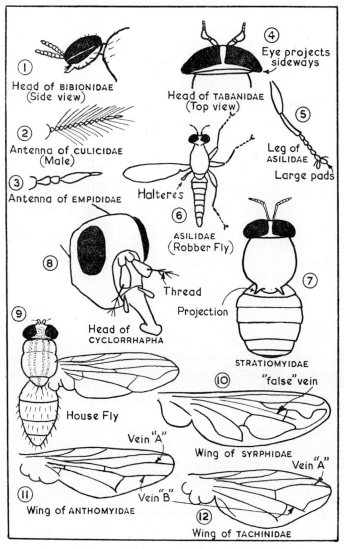

① Head of BIBIONIDAE (Side view)

② Antenna of CULICIDAE (Male)

③ Antenna of EMPIDIDAE

④ Eye projects sideways

Head of TABANIDAE (Top view)

⑤ Leg of ASILIDAE

Large pads

Halteres

⑥ ASILIDAE (Robber Fly)

⑧ Head of CYCLORRHAPHA

Thread

Projection

⑦ STRATIOMYIDAE

⑨ House Fly

⑩ "false" vein

Wing of SYRPHIDAE

⑪ Vein "A"

Vein "B"

Wing of ANTHOMYIDAE

⑫ Vein "A"

Wing of TACHINIDAE

PLATE 12. DIPTERA

2. Antennae

    (a) short [*see* Plate 12 (1)]; (insect stoutly built)   .
                         FAMILY *BIBIONIDAE* (p. 74)

    (b) long; (insect delicate)   3

3. Wings

    (a) with some shiny scales   .   .   .   .   .
                         FAMILY *CULICIDAE* (p. 74)

    (b) without any scales .   .   .   .   .
                    FAMILY *CHIRONOMIDAE* (p. 74)

KEY TO THE FAMILIES OF BRACHYCERA

1. Body

    (a) thickly clad with hairs so as to resemble a humble
         bee; (a long tongue may project from the
         head) .   .FAMILY *BOMBYLIIDAE* (p. 76)

    (b) not resembling a humble bee   2

2. Legs

    (a) long, strong and densely covered with sharp
         spikes and bristles, either large pads on the
         feet [*see* Plate 12 (5) and (6)] *or* abdomen very
         long.   .   FAMILY *ASILIDAE* (p. 75)

    (b) slender and with few or no strong spikes .   .   3

3. Body

    (a) thickly covered with hairs (wings dark)   .   .
                     FAMILY *THEREVIDAE* (p. 76)

    (b) not very hairy, or hairless   4

4. Eyes

    (a) very large, extending sideways [*see* Plate 12 (4)];
         (fast fliers) .   FAMILY *TABANIDAE* (p. 75)

    (b) rounded, not extending sideways   .   .   .   5

5. Body colour

  (*a*) metallic sheen; abdomen usually short; two or
    more backward pointing projections on the
    thorax [*see* Plate 12 (7)] . . . .
        FAMILY *STRATIOMYIDAE* (p. 75)
  (*b*) drab; abdomen elongated; no backward point-
    ing projections on thorax; antennae [*see* Plate
    12 (3)] . FAMILY *EMPIDIDAE* (p. 76)

KEY TO THE FAMILIES OF CYCLORRHAPHA

1. Habits

  (*a*) often found hovering in the air; (often with black
    and yellow striping[1] . . . . .
        FAMILY *SYRPHIDAE* (p. 76)
  (*b*) not as above 2

2. Lobes at base of wings

  (*a*) very small or absent 3
  (*b*) well developed 4

3. Head

  (*a*) very large; (antennae long, or very long and
    clubbed) . FAMILY *CONOPIDAE* (p. 76)
  (*b*) not large; (antennae short) . . . .
        FAMILY *CORDYLURIDAE* (p. 76)

4. Mouth-parts

  (*a*) none visible . FAMILY *OESTRIDAE* (p. 77)
  (*b*) plainly visible 5

5. Vein "B" [*see* Plate 12 (11) and (12)]

  (*a*) parallel to vein "A" or bent slightly towards it
    [*see* Plate 12 (11)]. . . . . .
        FAMILY *ANTHOMYIDAE* (p. 77)

---

[1] A confirmatory character for SYRPHIDAE: in the wing there is a "false
vein," i.e. one which has no connection with any other vein [*see* Plate 12 (10)].

(*b*) bent very sharply towards vein "A" [*see* Plate
12 (12)][1]   . FAMILY *TACHINIDAE* (p. 78)

NOTES ON THE FAMILIES OF DIPTERA

FAMILY *TIPULIDAE*. Crane flies or Daddy-long-legs.
Slow and clumsy in flight. Their larvae include the "leather-
jackets" which are pests of grassland and of cereal crops, on
whose roots they feed. The larvae of other species live in wood,
and some in water. The adults are often found in damp
places.

FAMILY *CULICIDAE*. Gnats and mosquitoes. Members of
this family have the mouth-parts highly adapted for sucking.
They are drawn out into a fine pointed dagger. The males suck
plant juices, but the females suck the blood of mammals. In
parts of Europe some mosquitoes are carriers of malaria, but while
their "stab" causes great irritation to some people, our species
do not carry the disease. All their larval life is spent in the water,
either in ponds or in holes in rotting wood.

There are two main groups, and in each the males may be
distinguished by their feathery antennae [*see* Plate 12 (2)]—

Culicines. The body is held parallel to the surface on
which the insect is resting. *Culex pipiens* is the commonest
species.

Anophelines. The body is held inclined to the surface. *Ano-
pheles maculipennis* is our commonest species, it has spotted wings.
On the continent it carries malaria.

FAMILY *CHIRONOMIDAE*. Midges. They resemble the
Culicidae, but lack the scales on the wings, and also the wings
are always shorter than the abdomen. The males usually have
feathery antennae. The eggs are laid in the water, and the adults
swarm near water in large numbers. They can be a nuisance
merely because of their numbers, and some species can inflict
painful "stabs."

FAMILY *BIBIONIDAE*. They are often seen in swarms,
mating on the wing in early summer. The males can be

---

[1] The common House fly [*see* Plate 12 (9)] is an exception. It belongs to the
ANTHOMYIDAE but its wing venation resembles that of TACHINIDAE.

distinguished by their large eyes, which occupy nearly the whole head.

There are two genera which can be separated by examining the knee joint between thigh and shank on the fore-leg. *Bibio*, a large spike projects from the knee. *Dilophus*, a cluster of small spikes projects from the knee. Our commonest species is *Bibio marci*, the St. Mark's fly, entirely black, 10 mm, legs long and powerfully built.

FAMILY *STRATIOMYIDAE*. The backwards projecting projections on the thorax serve for spotting most members of this family at a glance. However, in some species they are missing. The body varies greatly in shape and colour; head, thorax and abdomen may be differently coloured. They usually have a metallic sheen. They are often found near water.

FAMILY *TABANIDAE*. Horse flies and clegs. These include some of the commonest flies of the countryside. Their mouth-parts are modified to form short stout stabbing organs, and their "bite" is painful but not poisonous. The large eyes projecting sideways provide a good spotting feature. We have three genera.

1. Antennae
    (a) [see Plate 12 (4)] . . . . *Tabanus*
    (b) [see Plate 12 (4)]; not as in this, but longer . 2

2. Antennae
    (a) first joint enlarged . . . *Haematopota*
    (b) first joint not enlarged, (gleaming eyes) . .
                                                   Chrysops

FAMILY *ASILIDAE*. Robber flies. Nearly all members of this family may be spotted by means of the large pads on the feet [see Plate 12 (5)]. All are fierce fast-flying insects, and will attack almost any other. The mouth-parts form a short but powerful stabbing organ. The genus *Leptogaster* lacks the pads but has instead very long, almost straight claws and a very slender abdomen, total length 10 mm. *Asilus crabroniformis*, our largest species, 28 mm, black and yellow abdomen, yellowish wings. Most other Asilidae are about 12 mm and of dull coloration.

FAMILY *THEREVIDAE.* The mouth-parts are somewhat similar to those of Asilidae (above), but neither so hard nor so pointed.

FAMILY *EMPIDIDAE.* The mouth-parts form a sharp dagger as in Asilidae (above). The largest and commonest species is *Empis tessellata*, 10 mm, dagger 3.5 mm, grey colour. All the other species are much smaller, and in some of them dagger is scarcely visible. In the males of *Hilara* the first joint of the fore-foot is swollen; the males and females may be caught mating over water.

FAMILY *BOMBYLIIDAE.* Bee flies. These easily recognized insects hover around flowers, sucking the nectar by means of the long "tongue." The eggs are laid near the nests of solitary bees and, on hatching, the larvae feed on the bee larvae. *Bombylius major*, our largest species, 10 mm not including the length of the folded wings.

FAMILY *SYRPHIDAE.* Hover flies. It is difficult to give a simple structural feature for these flies, though in practice it is not difficult to spot the family. They are usually to be found hovering over flowers, or, on dull days, actually resting on the more showy flowers such as yellow Compositae. The hovering habit, however, is by no means confined to this family or even to the Diptera. The false vein character (p. 73[1]) affords good confirmation. Not all Syrphidae have the brown and yellow markings, but many do, and for this reason coupled with their liking for flowers, they are often confused with bees. They have, however, no sting and are quite harmless.

FAMILY *CORDYLURIDAE.* A large family of small and medium sized flies. They are often to be found on rotting fruit or meat. One of the commonest is *Scopeuma stercorarium*, 13 mm with wings folded, body thickly clothed with golden yellow hairs in the male and greenish hairs in the female. They occur in large numbers on dung in the summer.

FAMILY *CONOPIDAE.* A small family of active flies which lay their eggs on bees and wasps. The larvae live inside these insects.

Key to the Genera

1. Antennae
   - (a) long and ending in a club 2
   - (b) short 3

2. Abdomen
   - (a) with a narrow "waist" . . *Physocephala*
   - (b) without a "waist" . . . . *Conops*

3. Wings
   - (a) slightly spotted with grey . . *Myopa*
   - (b) clear, not spotted . . . . . *Sicus*

FAMILY *OESTRIDAE*. A small family of economic importance. The adults live for only a short time, have no mouth-parts and do not feed. They lay their eggs on the skin of farm animals, from which they are either licked off or burrow through the animal's skin. Part of the life-history takes place inside the body of the host, causing irritation and damage.

Key to the Commoner Genera

1. Lobes at base of wing
   - (a) very small . . *Gasterophilus* (horse bot-fly)
   - (b) not small 2

2. Abdomen
   - (a) densely hairy . . *Hypoderma* (ox warble-fly)
   - (b) not densely hairy . . *Oestrus* (sheep bot-fly)

FAMILY *ANTHOMYIDAE*. A very large family.

Key to some of the Most Common Genera

1. Wing venation
   - (a) resembling that shown in Plate 12 (9) . .
     Musca
   - (b) not resembling the above 2

2. Head

    (*a*) with stiff dagger projecting forwards   .   .

                                           Stomoxys

    (*b*) without a stiff dagger [for wing *see* Plate 12 (11)]

                                           Fannia

The genus *Musca* includes the house fly *Musca domestica* [*see* Plate 12 (9)] and the autumn house fly *Musca autumnalis*. *M. domestica* is found in and around houses during the summer and is a major threat to health. It feeds on decaying matter and human refuse, and it may travel from there to human food on which it deposits the causative organisms of several diseases, e.g. typhoid, dysentery and summer diarrhoea. *M. autumnalis* differs from it in having a thin streak of black between the eyes (view the head from above) instead of a broad band. It is not dangerous as it enters houses in autumn for shelter only, and does not come into contact with human food. *Fannia* is not a harmful fly. *Stomoxys* is the stable fly, 10 mm. It is a blood sucker, and its dagger can inflict a large and painful wound.

FAMILY *TACHINIDAE*. A very large family. The following descriptions fit some of the largest groups. Their habits are varied. Metallic blue coloration . . . Blue bottles, *Calliphora*. Metallic green coloration . . . Green bottles, *Lucilia*. Abdomen marbled black and grey . . . Flesh fly, *Sarcophaga*. Very hairy, especially on the thorax. Olive green colour. Often occurring in clusters. . . Cluster fly, *Pollenia*.

INTRODUCTION TO SPIDERS

SPIDERS may be recognized either by the structure of the body, or by the situations in which they are found. Both of these should be noted carefully in order to be certain of the identification of the animal, and to learn as much as possible about it.

All spiders have their bodies clearly divided into two parts. The front part corresponds to a combination of the head and the thorax of an insect, since it bears the eyes, the mouth-parts and mouth, and the legs. It will be referred to as the "*head-thorax*" (the word normally used is "cephalothorax"). The word "head" will be used to describe the fore-part of this, the region of the eyes. These lie on the upper surface, or at the front. They are usually eight in number, but there may be less. They are smooth, and not faceted like those of insects, and are therefore called "*simple eyes.*" The mouth-parts consist of a pair of *maxillae* on the under-surface of the head, and a pair of *chelicerae* below the eyes. These chelicerae each have a thin, pointed fang at the end, which has a duct that allows poison to run into the wounds that they inflict on the spider's prey [*see* Plate 14 (2)]. There are a pair of antenna-like *pedipalps*, one on either side of the mouth, and pointing forward. The last joint of these has, in the adult male, a swelling by which the sex may be recognized. There are eight *legs*, of which two pairs usually point forwards, the other two pairs being directed backwards.

The hinder part of the body, or *abdomen*, is joined to the head-thorax by a thin stalk, the *pedicel*. The abdomen has, at its rear end, the *spinners*. These are the openings through which the spider's silk is shed after being produced by glands inside the abdomen. They are seen as conical organs, four or six in number. On the under-surface of the abdomen are the openings of the "lungs" and the genital openings, quite large in the female. Neither the abdomen nor the head-thorax is divided into segments as in the insects.

Spiders either hunt for their food, which generally consists of insects, or they spin a web to act as a trap, and wait for insects to be caught. Notice should always be taken of a web, as this will often serve to determine the family of the builder, merely by its construction and situation.

The key that follows can mostly be used with the aid of a ×8 hand lens only. With smaller spiders, however, a larger magnification is needed. Specimens should be carefully placed in specimen-tubes of sufficient size. If they are to be killed, this should be done with the fumes of Ethyl Acetate. The dead spiders should be kept in 80 per cent alcohol, and examined immersed in liquid. Examination should always be carried out in bright sunlight, or at least in daylight.

KEY TO THE COMMONER FAMILIES
OF SPIDERS

1. Spinners
   (a) project beyond the end of the abdomen, and may be seen from above 2
   (b) not seen from above 4

2. Anterior Spinners
   (a) touching each other [Abdomen pattern as in Plate 15 (1)] . . . . . .
   FAMILY *ANYPHAENIDAE* (p. 104)
   (b) touching each other [Abdomen pattern *not* as in Plate 15 (1)] . . . . . .
   FAMILY *CLUBIONIDAE* (p. 19)
   (c) not touching 3

3. Colour
   (a) dark: no pattern . . . . . .
   FAMILY *GNAPHOSIDAE* (p. 92)
   (b) brown, with lighter brown or yellow patterns
   FAMILY *AGELENIDAE* (p. 93)

4. Legs
   (a) first three pairs of legs spread forwards and sideways [*see* Plate 13 (1)] (for exceptions *see* p. 95) . . . . . .
   FAMILY *THOMISIIDAE* (p. 94)
   (b) first two pairs of legs directed forwards, last two pairs, backwards 5

5. Legs
   (a) very long and thin (up to 36 mm long) Eyes [*see* Plate 16 (1)] . . . . .
   FAMILY *PHOLCIDAE* (p. 96)
   (b) "normal" thickness and length . . . 6

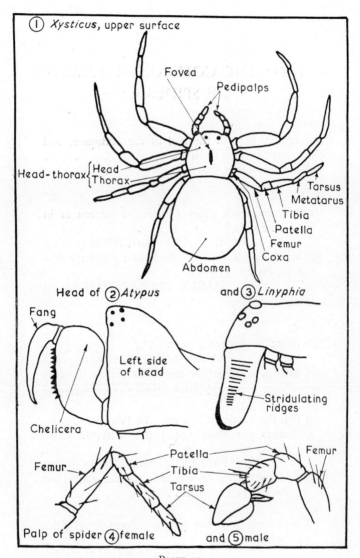

1 *Xysticus*, upper surface

Fovea

Pedipalps

Head-thorax { Head / Thorax

Tarsus
Metatarus
Tibia
Patella
Femur
Coxa

Abdomen

Head of 2 *Atypus*   and 3 *Linyphia*

Fang

Left side
of head

Chelicera

Stridulating
ridges

Femur

Patella
Tibia
Tarsus

Femur

Palp of spider 4 female   and 5 male

PLATE 13

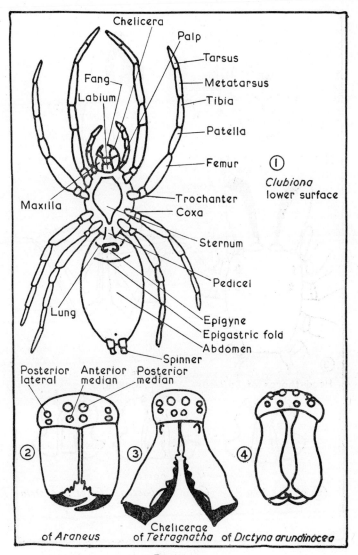

Chelicera

Palp

Tarsus

Metatarsus

Tibia

Patella

Femur

① *Clubiona* lower surface

Fang

Labium

Trochanter

Coxa

Maxilla

Sternum

Pedicel

Epigyne

Epigastric fold

Abdomen

Lung

Spinner

Posterior lateral

Anterior median

Posterior median

② of *Araneus*

③ Chelicerae of *Tetragnatha*

④ of *Dictyna arundinacea*

PLATE 14

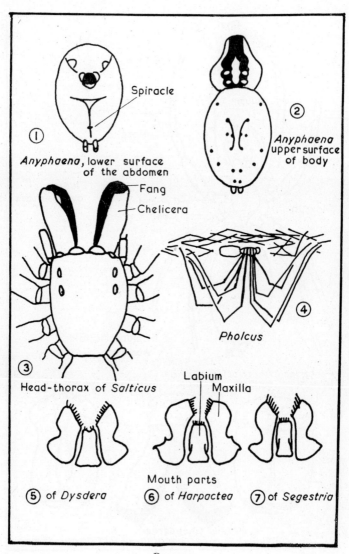

Spiracle

① *Anyphaena*, lower surface of the abdomen

② *Anyphaena* upper surface of body

Fang
Chelicera

④ *Pholcus*

③ Head-thorax of *Salticus*

Labium
Maxilla

Mouth parts

⑤ of *Dysdera*   ⑥ of *Harpactea*   ⑦ of *Segestria*

PLATE 15

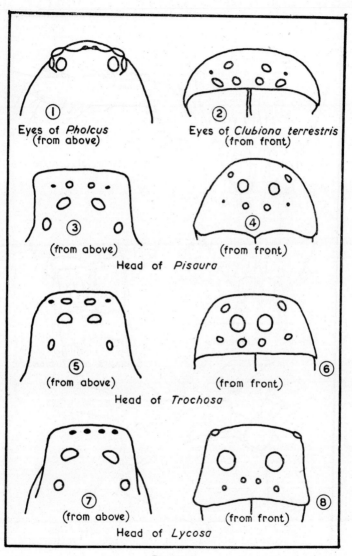

① Eyes of *Pholcus*
(from above)

② Eyes of *Clubiona terrestris*
(from front)

③ (from above)

④ (from front)

Head of *Pisaura*

⑤ (from above)

⑥ (from front)

Head of *Trochosa*

⑦ (from above)

⑧ (from front)

Head of *Lycosa*

PLATE 16

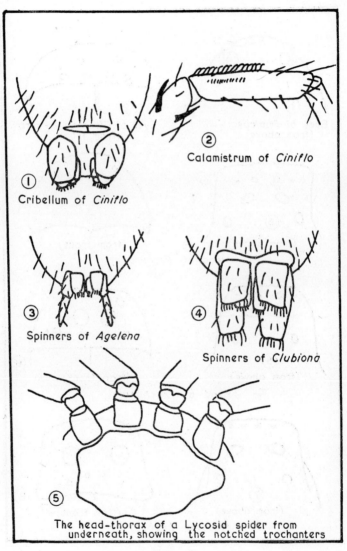

① Cribellum of *Ciniflo*

② Calamistrum of *Ciniflo*

③ Spinners of *Agelena*

④ Spinners of *Clubiona*

⑤ The head-thorax of a Lycosid spider from underneath, showing the notched trochanters

PLATE 17

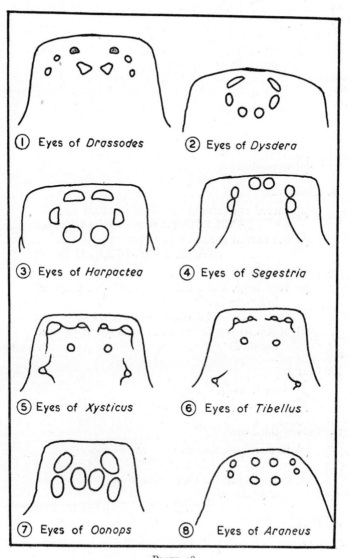

① Eyes of *Drassodes*

② Eyes of *Dysdera*

③ Eyes of *Harpactea*

④ Eyes of *Segestria*

⑤ Eyes of *Xysticus*

⑥ Eyes of *Tibellus*

⑦ Eyes of *Oonops*

⑧ Eyes of *Araneus*

PLATE 18

6. Chelicerae

    (*a*) very large and prominent with fangs pointing downwards [*see* Plate 13 (2)]   .   .   .
                      FAMILY *ATYPIDAE* (p. 96)

    (*b*) normal size, or large, but with fangs pointing inwards, towards each other   .   .   .   7

7. Chelicerae

    (*a*) long [*see* Plate 14 (3)]   8
    (*b*) normal size   9

8. Chelicerae

    (*a*) curved outwards at their ends [*see* Plate 14 (3)] .
             FAMILY *TETRAGNATHIDAE* (p. 96)

    (*b*) not curved outwards, [*see* Plate 14 (4)]   .   .
                FAMILY *DYSDERIDAE* (p. 97)

9. First row of eyes

    (*a*) very large, and looking forward (head square) [*see* Plate 15 (3)]   .   .   .   .   .
                FAMILY *SALTICIDAE* (p. 98)

    (*b*) of similar size to the other eyes (front of head rounded)   10

10. Eyes in

    (*a*) three rows (4, 2 and 2)   11
    (*b*) two rows (4 and 4) *or* six only in number   .   12

11. Eyes of third row

    (*a*) further apart than those of the second   .   .
                FAMILY *PISAURIDAE* (p. 100)

    (*b*) only slightly further apart than those of the second row   .   .   .   .   .   .
                FAMILY *LYCOSIDAE* (p. 100)

12. Eyes

    (*a*) six in number, in a close group   .   .   .
                FAMILY *OONOPIDAE* (p. 103)

    (*b*) eight in number, in clear rows   .   .   .   13

13. Colour

  (a) green, or green and scarlet   .   .   .   .
                FAMILY *SPARRASSIDAE* (p. 103)

  (b) not green all over   14

14. Eyes

  (a) white, except for the anterior medians, which
        are dark   FAMILY *DICTYNIDAE* (p. 103)

  (b) all dark   15

15. Inner margin of chelicerae

  (a) without teeth   .   .   .   .   .   .
                FAMILY *THERIDIIDAE* (p. 104)

  (b) with teeth   17

16. Maxillae

  (a) widest at the tips (anterior)   .   .   .   .
                FAMILY *ARGIOPIDAE* (p. 107)

  (b) widest at the bases (posterior) .   .   .   .
                FAMILY *LINYPHIIDAE* (p. 110)

SOME COMMON SPIDERS

THE following list of family characteristics may prove helpful as an alternative or supplement to the family key.

ATYPIDAE. Large spiders living in silk tubes that protrude from a hole in the ground. The chelicerae are very large, and strike downwards.

ANYPHAENIDAE. The upper surface of the abdomen has quite characteristic markings [*see* Plate 15 (2)].

TETRAGNATHIDAE. The sternum is pointed, the chelicerae are very long, curving outwards, and bearing very long fangs [*see* Plate 14 (3)].

THERIDIIDAE. Found in a web of crossing strands, with no apparent order. Small spiders.

THOMISIIDAE. Second legs are the longest, often with the first three pairs of legs directed forwards and sideways. The second row of eyes curved forwards at its ends.

SALTICIDAE. Small spiders, spinning no web. The front of the head is straight, with four large eyes looking forwards. Legs fairly short and stout.

ARGIOPIDAE. Spinning an orb-web [*see* Plate 20 (1)]. There are three tarsal claws, and the maxillae are widest at the tips.

AGELENIDAE. The anterior spinners protrude behind the end of the abdomen. Medium- or large-sized spiders spinning a cob-web [*see* Plate 20 (2)].

LYCOSIDAE. Spin no web, and are found running. The second and third rows of eyes are about equal in length. In summer females may carry a cocoon fixed to the spinners.

PISAURIDAE. These are large spiders, spinning no web, and running about like the Lycosidae. The third row of eyes is much longer than the second. In summer the female may be seen carrying a cocoon in her chelicerae.

PHOLCIDAE. Legs are very long and thin, and the abdomen is cylindrical. They are usually found indoors, where they hang upside-down in their webs.

LINYPHIIDAE. Found upside-down in a flat "hammock-web." The maxillae are widest at the rear end. These are usually small spiders.

GNAPHOSIDAE. Spiders usually hidden by day. There is no pattern, but there is a covering of dark, velvety hairs. The anterior median eyes are often darker than the others, and the posterior median eyes oval or triangular. The spinners project behind the posterior end of the abdomen.

CLUBIONIDAE. Resembling the Gnaphosidae, except that the anterior spinners are touching, and not set apart from each other. They are more frequently found on vegetation than the Gnaphosidae, and, in general, are lighter in colour.

DYSDERIDAE. Strong chelicerae, with a very long fang. The head-thorax is brown, red or orange, and the abdomen light-coloured. There are only six eyes.

DICTYNIDAE. Webs have a blue tinge. The eyes in two nearly straight rows, and pearly white, except for the anterior medians, which are darker. The anterior spinners are separated, and the cribellum may be seen as an oval or rectangular area in front of the spinners [see Plate 17 (1)]. The female has a claw on the pedipalp.

OONOPIDAE. Brick-red spiders without a pattern. The legs are yellow, and there are six large eyes.

SPARRASSIDAE. Large spiders. The female is green, the male green with scarlet stripes on the abdomen. Otherwise, they are similar to the Clubionidae.

FAMILY *CLUBIONIDAE*. A family of medium-sized spiders, usually of yellow or brown coloration. *Clubiona* is a genus with many species, several of them quite common. To tell them apart without a microscope is very difficult in some cases. In general the size may vary between 4 and 11 mm. *C. corticalis* can be recognized by the pattern on the abdomen —a dark median line followed by several V-shaped marks, all on a light background. The sternum is light brown, and has a darker border. This species lives in the open, but, by day, is usually found under cover such as stones or logs. *C. reclusa* favours damp places and woods. Its length varies between 5 and 9 mm. The abdomen is dark brown, and sometimes there is an even darker dorsal stripe. The sternum is similar to that of *C. corticalis*. The female has brown legs, the male has yellow legs. *C. pallidula* is found in bushes or woods, and is of much the same size as the last species. The chelicerae, abdomen, sternum and head are all dark brown. The thorax is lighter, but with a thin, median stripe. The legs are yellow. *C. terrestris* is slightly smaller, ranging from 5 to 7 mm in length. It is commonly found hiding in cracks in the bark of bushes or trees, or under stones. The abdomen is yellow usually with a red-brown dorsal stripe. The head-thorax, sternum and legs are yellow. *C. trivialis* is found in dry, open spaces, and in gorse and heather. It is somewhat smaller, between 3 and 5 mm long. The head-thorax, sternum and abdomen are yellow-brown or red-brown. The legs are very light coloured, particularly in females. *Cheiracanthum erraticum* is 5 to 8 mm in length. It is fairly common on low vegetation. The colour is yellowish-green. There is no obvious fovea on the head. The abdomen has a median dorsal red stripe. The chelicerae are very long and have black ends. *Agroeca proxima* is 4 to 8 mm long. It is found in woods and heaths. The head-thorax is narrow in front, and light-brown in colour, with darker stripes radiating from the centre. The abdomen is brown, with little or no pattern. *Zora spinimana* is 5 to 7 mm long. It has a yellow head-thorax with two longitudinal brown stripes. The abdomen is similar, and the sternum is yellow with brown marks between the bases of the legs. The eyes have a similar arrangement to those of the Lycosidae [*see* Plate 16 (2)].

FAMILY *GNAPHOSIDAE*. This is a family of small or medium sized spiders, usually hunting only at night. They are normally dark in colour, and have little or no pattern. The anterior median eyes are often darker than the others, and the posterior eyes are often not round, but square, or of some other shape. The abdomen is long and narrow, with spinners projecting beyond the posterior end. The two common genera, *Scotophaeus* and *Drassodes* are separated by the eyes. The anterior eyes of *Scotophaeus* are evenly spaced, and the anterior medians are larger than the anterior laterals. These are elliptical in shape. In *Drassodes*, however, the anterior median eyes are slightly smaller than the anterior laterals, and closer to the laterals than to each other. *Scotophaeus blackwalli* is nearly always found in houses or sheds, on the walls of which it hunts by night. It is covered with black hairs which give the inpression of smooth grey fur. Length, 8 to 11 mm. *Drassodes lapidosus* has a length of up to 20 mm. The colour is yellow-brown or red-brown. There is sometimes a darker mark along the fore part of the middle of the abdomen. *D. signifer* is about half the maximum length of the last species. It is covered with short, dark hairs, which make the ground-colour somewhat darker, almost black. The abdomen has a similar dorsal stripe, sometimes with light spots on each side of it, and V-shaped marks behind it.

FAMILY *AGELENIDAE*. Mostly medium- or large-sized spiders, some of which live indoors—the house-spiders. The backwardly projecting spinners form an obvious recognition character. They are very often found in webs such as the untidy cobweb found in undisturbed corners of walls, windows, etc. [*see* Plate 20 (2)]. *Textrix denticulata* (body-length, 8 mm) is usually found in crevices under stones and other objects. The body-colour is black, and the last row of eyes curves backwards at its ends. The legs have alternate light and dark bands. *Agelena labyrinthica* is known as the "labyrinth spider." It spins a large white web on gorse-bushes or grass. These webs may be seen from twenty yards away, or further, and there is an escape-tunnel of silk leading away from the lowest part of the web, which the spider will use if it is molested. The head-thorax is brown, with dark edges. Both rows of eyes curve forwards. The abdomen is dark, with a series of light V-shaped marks on the posterior part. The length of the body is up to 12 mm. *Amaurobius atropos* is not so large (10 mm) as *Agelena* but is otherwise similar in appearance. It prefers damp places and may be found under such cover as stones or logs. It does not spin a conspicuous web. The head is black, and the eyes are not in strongly-curved rows. *Tegenaria domestica* is the commonest of the house-spiders. It may be 10 mm or more in length. The head-thorax is light brown with black edges. The abdomen is very pale brown with dark spots. *T. atrica* is also found in houses, as well as in the open. The head-thorax has dark, radiating marks, and the abdomen a median brown stripe, with other lines running outwards from it. It is a very large spider, up to 15, or even 19 mm long. The legs are very long and spiny. *T. silvestris* is similar in appearance, but much smaller—up to 8 mm. It spins its web in woods and under bushes.

FAMILY *THOMISIIDAE*. This family includes the "Crab-spiders," so-called because of the round, flat abdomen, the large first pair of legs, and the habit of running backwards and side-ways. A few species have a quite different shape. The spiders of this family spin no webs, and do not hunt very actively. Typically, they lie concealed, and pounce on any suitable insect that passes sufficiently close to their hiding-place. This habit of lurking under stones and other objects is held to explain the flattened abdomen of the typical form. The genera may be separated by the following key. The term "eye-space" means the space on the head having the anterior and posterior median eyes as its four corners.

1. Eye-space
   (*a*) square, or broader than long 2
   (*b*) longer than broad 3

2. Eye-space
   (*a*) anterior eyes equidistant and equal sized . .
   Misumena
   (*b*) anterior median eyes closer to the laterals than to each other, and smaller than the laterals . .
   Xysticus

3. Eye-space
   (*a*) narrower in front . . . . .*Diaea*
   (*b*) Not narrower in front . . . *Oxyptilopa*

The two common genera which are not crab-like are *Philo-dromus*, in which the posterior row of eyes curves slightly backwards, with the median eyes nearer to the laterals than to each other, and *Tibellus*, in which the posterior row of eyes is strongly curved backwards, and the posterior median eyes are close together. The abdomen is long and thin. *Diaea dorsata* is 3 to 6 mm long. It is found in trees and bushes. The female is bright green, with a brown patch on the upper surface of the abdomen. The male is reddish-brown, with a yellow line along the middle of the abdomen. The first two pairs of legs are very long. *Misumena vatia* may vary between 4 and 10 mm long, and is often found in flowers. The colour of the broad stripe on the head-thorax, and of the abdomen, varies from white, through yellow, to pink, and often matches the colour of the flower in which the spider lurks. It is even said that the individual spider can change colour to match the flower in which it lurks. This method of concealment helps the spider to catch insects visiting flowers for pollen or nectar. *Xysticus cristatus* is commonly found in grass and low vegetation. Its body-length is 4 to 7 mm. The head-thorax is brown with a wide, white median band, with a brown triangle in the centre. The abdomen is a pale brown with a darker central patch. The legs are white with brown markings. The colouring of the male is darker than that of the female. *X. audax* is often found on gorse. It is similar in size and pattern to the last species, except that the posterior corner of the dark triangle on the head is rounded rather than pointed. *Oxyptilopa praticola* is found on grass and low plants. Its body-length is 3 to 4 mm. The head-thorax has a red-brown central band, flanked by dark-brown or black. The abdomen is grey, with black spots and stripes. The sternum is yellow with a brown or black spot at the base of each leg, and a median brown mark in the posterior part. *O. trux* is of similar size, and found in similar places. The head-thorax of the female is light brown, that of the male dark brown. The female has a median yellow band flanked by two thin black lines on the head. The abdomen of both sexes is brown with transverse black markings. The legs are yellow, but the femora of the first two pairs are black in the male. *Philodromus aureolus* is quite common on grass, bushes and undergrowth. The female is 5 to 6 mm long, the male about 4 mm. The head-thorax is brown with a cream median band. The abdomen is brown, darker at the sides. On the upper surface it has dark spots and V-shaped marks. *Ph. dispar* is found in the same sort of places, and is of similar size. The

head-thorax is brown, with a cream triangle on the head.
The abdomen is fawn, usually with brown markings. *Tibellus
oblongus* is very common on grass, particularly in damp places.
The body-length of the female is 8 to 10 mm, that of the male,
7 to 8 mm. The male is bright grey, the female pale yellow.
There is a darker median band on the abdomen. There may be
a faint spot on each side of this mark.

FAMILY *PHOLCIDAE*. *Pholcus phalangoides* is the only
common species. It lives indoors, usually hanging downwards
from its untidy web. The head-thorax is small and rounded,
the abdomen long and cylindrical. The legs are very long and
thin [*see* Plate 15 (4)]. The colour is pale yellow, with black
patches on the abdomen.

FAMILY *ATYPIDAE*. *Atypus affinis* is a medium-sized
spider (9 to 12 mm) that lives in holes in banks. These holes are
dug by the spider, and are lined with silk, which is continued
outside the hole as a cylinder, lying on the surface of the earth.
The chelicerae are large and prominent, and the fangs point
downwards instead of inwards. This will distinguish the species
from any other in Britain. The head-thorax is red-brown in
colour; the abdomen is darker.

FAMILY *TETRAGNATHIDAE*. The genus *Tetragnatha*
spins orb-webs, and is sometimes included in the Argiopidae.
Pachygnatha, however, does not spin a web, and lives on the
ground. The most obvious family characteristic is the shape and
size of the chelicerae. [*see* Plate 14 (3)].

1. Abdomen

    (*a*) long and pointed .   .   .   (*Tetragnatha*)   2
    (*b*) normal .   .   .   .   (*Pachygnatha*)   4

2. Sternum

    (*a*) with yellow spot .   .   .   *T. extensa*
    (*b*) without yellow spot   3

3. Sternum

    (*a*) bright green (broad dark stripe on abdomen)   .
                                                  T. obtusa

 (*b*) brown (thin dark stripe on abdomen) . .
             T. montana

4. Head-thorax

 (*a*) dark brown (abdomen with yellow, black and white pattern) . . . . *P. degeeri*

 (*b*) yellow, with three dark stripes (abdomen yellow)
             P. clercki

T. extensa often builds its web near open water. It stays in the middle of the web with two pairs of legs stretched directly forwards and the other two pairs directed to the rear. Body-length, about 6 mm. *T. montana* usually builds its web away from water. *T. obtusa* is usually found in, or near, pine-woods, and is a larger spider than the other two species. Both species of *Pachygnatha* live under stones, or in undergrowth. *P. degeeri* is the smaller, with a length of only 3 to 4 mm.

 FAMILY *DYSDERIDAE.* The members of this family are medium- or large-sized spiders living in tubes or cells of silk, between stones, in crevices, under leaves and in similar sheltered positions. The palp of the female has a claw. The coxae of the first two pairs of legs are larger than those of the third and fourth pairs. There are only six eyes.

1. Eyes arranged

 (*a*) in a close group of six 2

 (*b*) in three separate pairs . . . *Segestria*

2. Eyes arranged

 (*a*) in a horse-shoe, open end in front . *Dysdera*

 (*b*) in a circle or oval (head-thorax dark brown, length of adult not more than 7 mm) . *Harpactea*

Segestria senoculata is up to 12 mm in length. The head-thorax is bright brown, the abdomen is light grey or yellow, with a series of triangular dark marks along the middle of the back. The femora of the legs are lighter in colour than the other segments. The first three pairs of legs are normally held forwards, the last pair pointing backwards. The first two pairs of legs are

stouter than the others. *Dysdera erythrina* has bright red-brown
legs and head-thorax, and a yellow abdomen with no pattern.
Body-length, 8 to 10 mm. *D. crocata* has a dark-brown head-
thorax, and a grey, or almost white, abdomen. Body-length,
9 to 15 mm. *Harpactea hombergii* has a brown head-thorax and a
brown or grey abdomen. Length of male, 5 to 6 mm, of female,
6 to 7 mm.

FAMILY *SALTICIDAE*. This is a family of small spiders
that hunt by jumping at small insects. The habit of leaping
means that the spiders must have comparatively good eyesight,
and this accounts for the four large anterior eyes, looking
forward.

1. Abdomen
    (*a*) black, with white transverse bars .   *Salticus*
    (*b*) without this "zebra" pattern   2

2. Eye-space[1]
    (*a*) broader behind than in front . .   .*Ballus*
    (*b*) not broader behind than in front .   .   3

3. Eye-space
    (*a*) slightly broader than long   .   .   . *Neon*
    (*b*) almost twice as broad as long .   .   .   4

4. Clypeus
    (*a*) narrower than diameter of anterior median eyes.   5
    (*b*) of normal width   6

5. Clypeus
    (*a*) as wide as half the diameter of the anterior median
        eyes .   .   .   .   .   *Evarcha*
    (*b*) even narrower than half the width of the anterior
        median eyes .   .   . *Heliophanus*

[1] The "eye-space" or "ocular trapezium" referred to is the area of the head
lying between the four posterior eyes. It is quite large in this family.

6. Colour

   (a) black, maybe with white spots on the abdomen.
   Sitticus
   (b) of head, black, of abdomen, brown .   *Euophrys*

Salticus scenicus is called the "zebra spider" because of the black
and white pattern on the abdomen. The male has very long
chelicerae and black front legs. Its other legs are brown, like
those of the female. It prefers exposed surfaces such as walls and
fences. The body length is 5 to 7 mm. *Heliophanus cupreus* is
found in low vegetation. The sternum and head-thorax are
black, the legs yellow with brown markings. The abdomen is
black in the male, but covered with shining green hairs in the
female. Length, 4 to 6 mm. *H. flavipes* is of similar size and
pattern, except that the legs are yellow unmarked with brown,
and the abdomen is grey in both sexes. *Ballus depressus* is found
in bushes and trees, and gives the impression of being flat and
short-legged. Its length is 4 to 5 mm. The head-thorax is black,
the abdomen of the male is dark brown, that of the female is
yellow with a median brown band, and brown sides. *Neon
reticulatus* has a very narrow clypeus. The head-thorax is yellow,
with black on the head, round the eyes. The abdomen is pale
yellow, with black reticulate markings, much more pronounced
in the male. It is found on the ground, in woods. Its length is
only 2 to 3 mm. *Euophrys frontalis* is only slightly larger, and is
found in short vegetation. The head is black, and the thorax
brown. The anterior eyes are surrounded by a fringe of hairs,
white in the female, orange in the male. The female has a light-
coloured abdomen, with horizontal rows of dark spots. The
male has a light brown abdomen with a dark band on each side
and a row of arrowhead marks in the centre. The legs are light
brown, except that the first legs of the male have white tarsi, and
the rest of these first legs are black. *E. erratica* is found on walls
and other bare surfaces. The head-thorax is similar to that of
the previous species. The abdomen is black, with rows of white
spots, and the legs are light brown. The body-length is 3 to
4 mm. *Sitticus pubescens* is grey or black. The abdomen sometimes has white spots. The legs are light brown with darker

rings. The length is 4 to 5 mm. *Evarcha falcata* is 5 to 7 mm long, and is found in woods. The head-thorax is black and the anterior eyes are surrounded by white hairs. The abdomen of the female is grey with lighter spots; that of the male has two black streaks, between which may be black markings. The legs are light brown, with the first pair, and the femora of the others black in the male. *E. arcuata* is found on heather and in low vegetation. The head-thorax is black, the abdomen grey, with darker markings in the female. The legs are light brown except for the femora and the upper half of the first legs of the male, which are black. Body-length, 5 to 7 mm.

FAMILY *PISAURIDAE.* A family of the wolf-spiders, which are so-called because they hunt their prey actively, using no web, trap or concealment. They may be told apart from the other family of wolf-spiders by the arrangement of the eyes [*see* Plate 16 (3)] and by the fact that the female carries her egg-cocoon in her chelicerae, and not attached to the spinners, as the Lycosids do. *Pisaura listeri* is a large spider found in fields and under hedges. The head-thorax is pale brown in the middle, with a slightly darker brown at the edges. The abdomen is still darker. Body-length, 12 to 15 mm. *Dolomedes fimbriatus* is a very large spider, up to 18 mm. long (probably the largest in Britain). It is usually found hunting near water. It is brown in colour, with a yellow stripe on each side of the head-thorax and abdomen.

FAMILY *LYCOSIDAE.* This is the larger of the two families of wolf-spiders. The female carries her cocoon attached to her spinners, a common sight in fields during the summer. The prevailing colour is brown, often with longitudinal stripes of lighter or darker colour. The arrangement of the eyes [*see* Plate 16 (5)] is the best method of distinguishing this family from the Pisauridae, and from other families.

1. Head

      (*a*) as in Plate 16 (7), with almost vertical sides (clypeus much wider than the diameter of the anterior median eyes) .   .   .   *Lycosa*

(b) as in Plate 16 (5), with sloping sides (clypeus *not* much wider than the diameter of the anterior median eyes 2

2. Median light band of head-thorax

    (a) with dark markings, or absent altogether . . 3
    (b) with no dark markings . . . (*Tarentula*) 5

3. Median light band

    (a) absent . . . . . . *Arctosa*
    (b) present 4

4. Eyes of second row

    (a) large (V-shaped mark on the head, pointing backwards). . . . . (*Pirata*) 6
    (b) not much bigger than those of first row (head without V-shaped mark) . . *Trochosa*

5. Sternum

    (a) with a light patch . . . *T. pulverulenta*
    (b) without light patch. . . . *T. barbipes*

6. Femora

    (a) annulated (no light patch round the eyes) . .
                                    P. hygrophilus
    (b) not annulated (eyes surrounded by a light area) .
                                    P. piraticus

Lycosa. This is much the commonest genus in the family. Most of the members are similar in size and appearance, and range from 4 to 8 mm in length. The best recognition character is the narrow, elevated head region, with four large eyes on the raised part. The head-thorax sometimes has three light stripes, but the pattern is very variable. The abdomen has a light streak, flanked by dark stripes with lighter areas on each side. *L. amentata* is very common in pastures. The head-thorax is dark brown, the abdomen grey-green, with black mottling at the sides. The chelicerae are light brown, with lighter tips and darker markings elsewhere. The femora are annulated. *L. lugubris* is common in or near woods. There is a broad median light stripe along the fore-part of the abdomen. The femora are annulated in the female, black in the male. *L. pullata* is another common species. The head is black, and there are no distinct light stripes on the head-thorax. The sternum often has a triangular yellow mark. The legs are red-brown, and the femora of the first pair are sometimes darker than the rest. *L. nigriceps* is sometimes found in trees or bushes, whilst the other species are almost always found on the ground. The colour is light yellow-brown. The median stripe on the head is expanded behind the eyes. The sternum may have yellow markings. *Arctosa perita* is 7 to 9 mm long. It is found on heaths, and in sandy country, where it may be found either in the open or in a burrow. The head-thorax is brown or grey, with a double marginal band. There are dark stripes radiating out from the fovea. On the upper surface of the abdomen are two pairs of obvious light-coloured spots, and some smaller ones. There is no pattern on the lower surface, which is dark grey or black. The sternum is black and the chelicerae dark brown. *Trochosa ruricola* is 8 to 14 mm long. The ground colour is brown, with median and lateral stripes on the head-thorax, of a lighter shade, and a similar median mark on the fore-part of the abdomen. There are other light markings on the abdomen. The sternum is light brown. It is usually found hidden by day. *T. terricola* is about the same size, and the pattern is similar. The stripes are not so well-defined, however, and there is a redder tinge on the ground-colour. The sternum is red-brown. *Tarentula pulverulenta* is 5 to 10 mm in length. It may be found in many parts of Britain. The head-thorax is dark brown with a broad median band of lighter colour. The abdomen is also dark brown, with a lighter dorsal area and black markings on the sides. The sternum is dark, with a light patch in the middle. *T. barbipes* is slightly larger, 8 to 12 mm long. It is very similar to *T. pulverulenta* in pattern and colouring, the best difference to note being in the sternum, which is without the central light patch. *Pirata hygrophilus* is 5 to 7 mm in length. It is most often seen near water, or even moving on the surface film. It may be found in

a silk tube opening near the water-edge. The colour is dark
brown, almost black. There is the usual head-thorax pattern of
light longitudinal stripes, and there may be light markings on
the abdomen. The sternum is dark, usually with a light area in
the middle. The femora of the legs are annulated. *P. piraticus* is
found in very similar situations, although the size-range is greater,
4 to 9 mm. The colour is lighter, and there are two brown
stripes within the central light streak of the head. There is a
narrow white area round the eyes. The sternum is light brown
with dark marks opposite each of the coxae.

FAMILY *OONOPIDAE*. *Oonops pulcher* is the only species
likely to be found, usually under stones, decaying vegetation or
other cover. It is a small spider, only 2 mm long. Its colour is
pink or red, with the legs yellow. It has six eyes, close together
in an H-shape on the front of the head [*see* Plate 18 (7)].

FAMILY *SPARRASSIDAE*. The only British species is
Micrommata virescens. This is unmistakable because of its colour.
The female is bright green with a median stripe of dark green on
the abdomen. The male is yellow-green, with three scarlet
stripes on the abdomen. The length of the female is 12 to 13 mm,
of the male, 8 mm. It spins no web, and hunts among vegetation,
like the wolf-spiders.

FAMILY *DICTYNIDAE*. A spider with a cribellum [*see*
Plate 17 (1)] or which spins a web of bluish silk probably
belongs to this family. The size, at least of the adult, separates
the genus *Ciniflo* from the others, which are more difficult
to identify. The eyes are all pearl-white, except the anterior
medians, which are darker. The pedipalp of the female carries
a claw.

1. Body-length
    (*a*) more than 5 mm .   .   .   . (*Ciniflo*)   2
    (*b*) less than 4 mm   3

2. Legs
    (*a*) with light and dark rings.   .   . *C. similis*
    (*b*) without rings.   .   .   .   . *C. ferox*

3. Anterior median eyes
    (*a*) much smaller than the others .   .   *Lathys*
    (*b*) not smaller .   .   .   .   .   *Dictyna*

Ciniflo similis is found in crevices of all sorts, including holes in walls, corners of sheds, window frames and similar places. It is a fairly large spider (female 9 to 12 mm, male 6 to 8 mm). There is a double dark median stripe on the fore-part of the abdomen. *C. ferox* is a larger, darker spider, found in the same sort of places as the other species. The female has a dark grey or black abdomen, the male has the last segment of the pedipalps white. Length, 8 to 14 mm. *Lathys humilis* is a small spider, about 2 mm long, found in bushes. The female has a light brown abdomen with a pair of darker brown bars, flanked by white dots. The male has a similar pattern, but a much darker, almost black, background. In both sexes the legs are light brown and have rings of darker colour. *Dictyna* is a genus including several species of small spiders. The head-thorax is dark brown and the head is elevated. The abdomen is light, with a broad dark median band broken into bars at its posterior end, in each of the two common species, *D. arundinacea* and *D. uncinata*. These two are very difficult to tell apart without the use of a microscope.

FAMILY *ANYPHAENIDAE*. There is only one British species, *Anyphaena accentuata*. This is about 6 mm long, and is commonly found in woodlands. Its head-thorax bears two dark and three lighter stripes on the upper surface. The abdomen is light-coloured with very clear black markings [*see* Plate 15 (2)]. The lower surface of the abdomen is darker, with a dark line running along the middle.

FAMILY *THERIDIIDAE*. These are generally small, bright spiders, spinning their webs in bushes. These webs consist of a set of threads criss-crossing apparently at random, in three dimensions. These threads entangle or impede crawling or flying insects which are caught by the spider leaving its "hide," built to one side of the web, and made of silk and rubbish such as old leaves. The spiders have a "comb" of hairs on the fourth tarsi, which may sometimes be seen with a strong lens. This

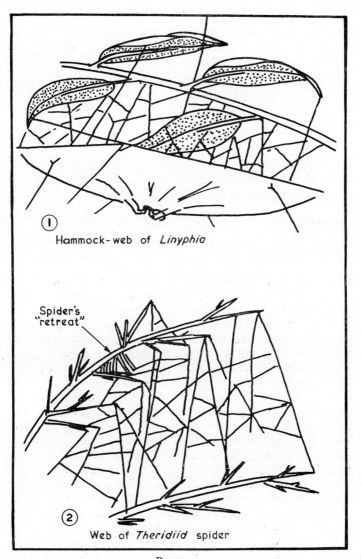

① Hammock-web of *Linyphia*

Spider's "retreat"

② Web of *Theridiid* spider

PLATE 19

comb is used for pulling out a wide band of silk from the spinners to cover an insect struggling in the web. Although the family is a large one, with several very common species, few of these are large and easy to distinguish.

1. Coxae of fourth legs
    (a) smaller than the others .   .   .   *Theridion*
    (b) not smaller than the others   2

2. Anterior row of eyes
    (a) curved forwards at the ends . . *Stearodea*
    (b) straight (eyes on tubercles)   .   .   .   3

3. Abdomen
    (a) fawn .   .   .   .   .   *Robertus*
    (b) black .   .   .   .   *Enoplognatha*

Theridion redimitum is very commonly found in bushes. The head-thorax is yellow, with a black median line and black edges. The abdomen may be yellow, with black spots (in two rows) or with a red oval mark, or the upper surface may be entirely red. These three varieties all have a broad median dark band on the under-surface of the abdomen. The body-length is 4 mm. *Theridion notatum* is also common in bushes. The head-thorax is brown, with darker stripes. The abdomen is very short and round. There is a median red stripe, with a brown stripe on either side. The legs are yellow with brown annulations. The body-length is 3 mm. *Th. denticulatum* may be found in bushes or on buildings and fences. It is brown, with a broad white area along the middle of the abdomen. The legs are annulated with darker brown. Length, 2 to 3 mm. *Stearodea bipunctata* is very common, especially in sheds and similar places. The head-thorax is black, the abdomen brown, with white on the anterior part and along the middle, in the form of patches, a line, or dots. There are four marks or dents actually in the upper surface of the abdomen. The legs are yellow, the body-length is 6 mm. *Robertus lividus* is smaller, about 3 mm long. It is found under cover, in damp situations. The head is brown, darker than the thorax. The abdomen is fawn with four black spots. *Eno-plognatha thoracica* is 4 mm long. The head-thorax and legs are brown. The abdomen is black with two rows of white dots.

FAMILY *ARGIOPIDAE*. These are probably the best known spiders, as they spin the wheel-like orb-web that is so familiar [*see* Plate 20 (1)]. This web alone is the best recognition mark of the family, since these spiders are seldom found far away from a web. An exception to this is the adult male, which builds no web of its own. It is in this family that the females have the worst reputation for killing the males. As with all other animals and plants, identification is easier and more certain if note is taken of the situation in which the specimen is found. In this case the size and structure of the orb-web and the actual position of the spider should be noted. Sometimes the spider will be found actually on the web, sometimes to one side, perhaps under cover. Some spiders make a small silk chamber nearby, connected to the centre of the web by a signal silk that transmits the vibrations caused by a captured and struggling insect. In general, these spiders have round abdomens and short legs.

1. Posterior end of sternum
   - (*a*) pointed 2
   - (*b*) rounded 3

2. Web
   - (*a*) always found in bushes, never quite upright in position . . . . . *Meta*
   - (*b*) found under cover, in sheds etc. built vertically . *Netiscus*

3. Posterior row of eyes
   - (*a*) curved backwards . . . . *Cyclosa*
   - (*b*) straight 4

4. Posterior eyes
   - (*a*) equidistant . . . . . *Zygiella*
   - (*b*) with the medians close together . . . 5

5. Longest pair of legs

    (a) the fourth   .   .   .   .   .   *Cercidia*

    (b) the first .   .   .   .   .   .   *Araneus*

Meta reticulata is a very common spider, and its web is almost always to be found in the South of Britain during the summer. This web is small and sloping. The abdominal pattern is variable, but the head-thorax always has a dark Y-shaped mark. Length, 5 to 8 mm. *M. merianae* is larger, 8 to 13 mm in length. It builds its web in similar situations. It is a darker spider, with a brown head-thorax with black edges. The abdomen is black and white. There are two yellow spots on the lower side of the abdomen. *Netiscus cellulanus* is 4 mm long. It is usually found indoors. The head-thorax is yellow with black margins and median band. The abdomen is almost spherical, yellow with black markings. The legs are comparatively long and thin. *Cyclosa conica* is 6 mm in length. It builds a small, neat web. This often has a vertical band of silk across it, on the middle of which the spider sits. The head-thorax is dark-brown, and raised at the posterior end. The abdomen is black underneath and brown at the sides, and there is a pale band along the back. There are four white ventral spots. The shape of the abdomen is unusual in that it is very high, and has also a backwards projection. *Zygiella atrica* builds a web of which one of the radial lines is not connected to any of the circular strands, leaving a free segment [*see* Plate 20 (1)]. This free radial strand is not in quite the same plane as the others and leads to a silk chamber in which the spider hides, thus acting as a signal line. This web is usually built in bushes. The head-thorax is yellow with black margins. The abdomen is grey with red-brown markings. The males have very long palps. The body-length is 7 mm. *Z. litterata* builds a similar web, but usually on fences or in window-frames. The pattern of the abdomen is darker, without the red markings. Length, up to 10 mm. *Araneus diadematus* is the well-known "garden cross spider" that builds the large web that can hardly go unnoticed, especially in gardens. The colour is brown, though the sternum is quite dark. There is a dark median patch on the upper surface of the abdomen, with thin white streaks and dots on it. The

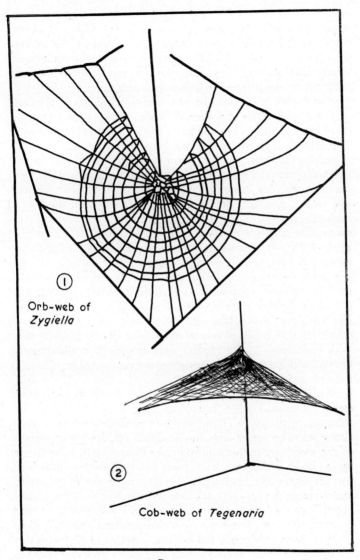

①
Orb-web of *Zygiella*

②
Cob-web of *Tegenaria*

PLATE 20

largest of these forms the conspicuous white cross that gives the
spider its name, and makes it quite unmistakable. The underside of the abdomen also has a dark median patch, outlined in
white. Body-length, up to 12 mm. *A. cucurbitina* is smaller,
only 6 mm long. It is common in gardens, especially in trees.
The head-thorax is bright brown, with black edges in the case
of the female. The abdomen is bright green, with a row of
small black spots on each side and a red spot at the posterior end.
The legs are brown, with black rings on those of the male.
A. reaumuri is larger, up to 13 mm in length. The head-thorax
is brown, the abdomen of varied colouring and pattern, but
usually with four elongated white spots on the upper surface,
and with a dark median band with white edges on the lower
surface. There are white markings round the spinners. *A.
sexpunctata* is about the same size. The colour, in general, is
black, with yellow markings on the upper surface of the abdomen, and two yellow patches on the lower surface. It lies
concealed near the web during the day, only emerging at night
to deal with any captured insects. *A. foliata* is 10 mm in length.
It commonly lives in bushes and tall grass. The head-thorax and
legs are light brown, the abdomen black, with a pattern of
white spots. *Cercidia prominens* has a light brown head-thorax,
with dark edges and a median dark stripe. The abdomen is
orange, and has a row of spines across the anterior edge. There is
a darker stripe down the centre.

FAMILY *LINYPHIIDAE*. These are small spiders, most
easily recognized when found on their web. This is a flat
structure, with maybe a loose mesh of threads crossing each other
above it. The spider lives upside-down on the lower surface
of the sheet or hammock portion [*see* Plate 19 (1)]. The larger
webs, built in bushes, often have a considerable number of
threads above the hammock. Smaller webs are often found
much nearer the ground, and usually have few such threads, or
none, since they are efficient in capturing walking insects rather
than flying ones. There are over two hundred British species,
most of them very small, and it is not intended to deal with this
group in any detail, as recognition is usually impossible without
the aid of a microscope and a comprehensive text-book. *Labulla*

thoracica is often found in houses, sheds and cellars. The head-thorax is yellow, with a darker patch. The abdomen has a pattern in different shades of brown. The female has a number of white spots on the lower surface of the abdomen. *Leptyphantes* is a genus containing some of the larger Linyphiid species. Most of these have a black abdomen with white transverse lines. Separation into species is not possible without a microscope. *Linyphia montana* very commonly builds its web in bushes. The head-thorax is brown with a median dark line and dark edges. The legs are pale yellow. The abdomen has a pattern of longitudinal brown lines, and often has small white spots on the upper surface. Length up to 7 mm. *L. resupina* is about 5 mm long and is common in similar places. The head-thorax and abdomen are dark brown, the under surface of the abdomen has four white spots on a dark brown or black background. The legs are brown with darker rings.

HARVESTMEN
(Opiliones)

JUST as spiders may be told apart from insects by the division of the body into only two distinct parts, instead of three, the Opiliones, or harvestmen (sometimes wrongly called "daddy-long-legs") may be identified by the lack of any division of the body at all. The body may be disc-shaped or egg-shaped, but there is no distinct head, thorax or abdomen. There may be, however, a division of the hind, or abdominal, end into segments, as is the case with insects (and certain very primitive tropical spiders).

A second distinguishing character is the great length and slenderness of the eight legs. There are other points of difference too, that may be seen on examination. The chelicerae are pincer-like [see Plate 21 (1)], but there are no poison glands in them. Harvestmen do not produce silk, so there are no spinners, and they make no web or snare. There are only two eyes, which are set up on a tubercle on the upper surface of the body, and facing outwards [see Plate 21 (2)]. The pedipalps are not unlike those of spiders, except that they more commonly have claws. The sexes are not always as easily separated as with adult spiders. They are nocturnal in habit, and hunt for their food, which is more varied than that of spiders. They will, at least in captivity, eat vegetable matter and insects already dead.

KEY TO FAMILIES AND SUB-FAMILIES

1. Ends of pedipalp
   - (a) with claw . . FAMILY *PHALANGIDAE*
   - (b) without claw . FAMILY *NEMASTOMATIDAE*

2. Palpal claw
   - (a) toothed 3
   - (b) not toothed 4

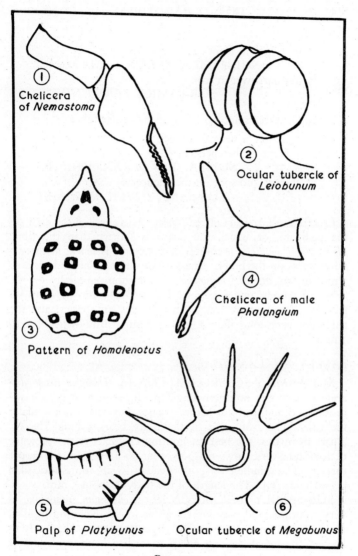

1 Chelicera of *Nemastoma*

2 Ocular tubercle of *Leiobunum*

3 Pattern of *Homalenotus*

4 Chelicera of male *Phalangium*

5 Palp of *Platybunus*

6 Ocular tubercle of *Megabunus*

PLATE 21

3. Body

    (*a*) narrower in front . . . . .
               SUB-FAMILY *SCLEROSOMATINAE*
    (*b*) not narrower in front . . . . .
               SUB-FAMILY *LEIOBUNINAE*

4. Group of three spines in front of the ocular tubercle

    (*a*) present; (a ventral projection from the first seg-
       ment of the chelicerae). . . . .
               SUB-FAMILY *OLIGOLOPHINAE*
    (*b*) absent; (no spur on the chelicerae) . . .
               SUB-FAMILY *PHALANGIINAE*

FAMILY *NEMASTOMATIDAE*. There is no tarsal claw on the pedipalp, of which the tarsus is shorter than the tibia. *Nemastoma lugubre* is a common species. It is black, with two white spots on the body. The legs are short. The body is 2 to 3 mm in length. *N. chrysomelas* is common, especially on the floors of woods, under leaves. The colour is brown, with no pattern. The legs are longer than in the last species, and the palps are very long indeed, up to 7 mm. Body-length, 2 to 3 mm.

FAMILY *PHALANGIDAE*

SUB-FAMILY *SCLEROSOMATINAE*. *Homalenotus quadri-dentatus* occurs in Southern England. It seems to have a head-thorax and abdomen, as separate parts, but this is not actually the case. The front end of the body bears a long "beak." Apart from this, the best recognition character is the presence of four transverse rows of spots, four to a row, on the upper surface. The middle two spots of each row are more noticeable [*see* Plate 21 (3)]. The length of the body is about 5 mm.

SUB-FAMILY *LEIOBUNINAE*. *Leiobunum rotundum* is very common, and may sometimes be found sheltering by day, under cover, in comparatively large numbers. The body is brown, the female having a darker median band, widening at the posterior end. The legs of both sexes are black, and very long, up to 6 cm. The length of the body is 4 to 7 mm. *L. blackwalli* is very similar in appearance to the last species, but there is always a white area round the eyes. Body-length, 3 to 6 mm.

SUB-FAMILY *OLIGOLOPHINAE*. *Mitopus morio* is pale yellow in colour, with a black median stripe, narrower in the middle of its length. The legs are marked with yellow and brown. The male is similar in pattern, but the general colour is darker. Length, 4 to 8 mm. *Oligolophus agrestis* is a very common species. The ground-colour is grey, with a dark median band with yellow or brown edges. The central spine of the trident is larger than the other two, and slightly in front of them. Length, 4 to 6 mm. *O. tridens* is very similar to the above species and also very common. The spines of the trident are equal in size, and are set in a straight line. Length, 4 to 6 mm. *Odiellus spinosus* is a large, southern form, with a length of 7 to 10 mm. The body is brown, with a darker median band, which has a straight posterior edge. The trident-spines are set horizontally, projecting in front of the carapace. The body is wide, and somewhat flat. *O. palpinalis* is similar in pattern, but smaller (body-length, 3 to 5 mm). The trident spines are vertical. The legs are ringed alternately in dark brown and yellow. *Lacinius ephippiatus* has a clearly marked black median band on a light yellow background. This band does not reach all the way back to the rear end of the body. Length, 4 to 6 mm.

SUB-FAMILY *PHALANGIINAE*. *Phalangium opilio* is a very common species, particularly in autumn. The body is brown above, with a darker marginal band in the case of the female, and dirty-white below. The male has very long palps and distinctively-shaped chelicerae [*see* Plate 21 (4)]. Size, 4 to 9 mm, the males much smaller than the females. *Opilio parietinus* is fairly common in late autumn. The colour is a blotchy brown, the undersurface being grey or yellow. Each coxa has a dark spot on it. Length, 6 to 8 mm. *Platybunus triangularis* may be found early in the spring. It may be recognized by the shape of the pedipalp [*see* Plate 21 (5)]. It is light brown in colour, and its length is 4 to 6 mm. *Megabunus diadema* may be recognized by the long, sharp spines on the ocular tubercle [*see* Plate 21 (6)]. It has a general black and white pattern, and is 3 to 5 mm long.

BOOK LIST

BOOKS ON INSECTS

GENERAL

IMMS, A. D. *A Text-book of Entomology*. Methuen. The standard text-book; essential for the school library.

Insect Natural History. Collins. The "New Naturalist" series. A fascinating book which takes the beginner through all aspects of insect life. Beautifully illustrated.

DALE, ALAN. *Patterns of Life*. Heinemann. Excellent both as a school text-book and as a general reader. Largely devoted to insects and contains several simple keys and illustrations. Many suggestions are given for field-work.

SANDARS, E. *An Insect Book for the Pocket*. Oxford University Press, Geoffrey Cumberledge. Much general information, good descriptions of families, with many illustrations. Only insects over half an inch in length are described. There are no keys. This is a pocket-book which really does fit into the pocket.

CHRYSTAL, R. NEIL. *Insects of the British Woodlands*. Warne. Several simple keys are provided, and also good descriptions which lead to the identification of many species. Technical terms are largely avoided. It covers a wide range of families, very attractive to the field biologist. Should provide material for the teacher planning field-work in forest districts.

ORTHOPTERA

HINCKS, W. D. *Handbooks for the Identification of British Insects. Dermaptera and Orthoptera*. Royal Entomological Society of London. This key is not easy to use, but with care leads to certain identification. For the teacher rather than the pupil.

ODONATA

LONGFIELD, C. *The Dragonflies of the British Isles*. Warne. Much valuable biological information. The coloured illustrations are excellent. The keys are based on colour, always a matter of opinion and therefore an unsatisfactory criterion. They require much practice before they can be used with confidence.

HEMIPTERA

MACAN, T. T. *A Key to the British Species of Corixidae with Notes on their Distribution*.

A Key to the British Water Bugs, excluding Corixidae with Notes on their Ecology. Both these keys are published by the Freshwater Biological Association of the British Empire. They are copiously illustrated but a binocular microscope is necessary for most identifications. The ecological notes should suggest many simple field-work projects.

LEPIDOPTERA

SOUTH, R. *Butterflies of the British Isles*. Warne.

Moths of the British Isles. Warne. By means of the coloured illustrations all British species of butterflies and moths can be identified, but the absence of keys makes this a slow process.

COLEOPTERA

JOY, N. *A Practical Handbook of British Beetles*. Witherby. Contains keys for the identification of all the British species, but inevitably uses many technical terms and calls for practice. Volume 1 contains keys and descriptions, Volume 2 illustrations. In the reference sections of most Public Libraries, should be in all School Libraries.

British Beetles, their Homes and Habitats. Warne. A good introduction. By means of the keys and illustrations many common species can be named. (The classification used varies slightly from that used in this book.)

HYMENOPTERA

STEP, E. *Bees, Wasps, Ants and Allied Orders of the British Isles.* Warne. Still the best general introduction to this order. There is much careful personal observation. The coloured illustrations give an idea of the range of forms but do not permit exact identification. No keys.

DONISTHORPE, H. *British Ants.* Routledge. The authoritative work on the family. Contains biological information and keys which are not always difficult if a binocular microscope is available.

DIPTERA

COLYER C. N. and HAMMOND, C. O. *Flies of the British Isles.* Warne. The only book covering the whole order. The keys are not easy to use, but the illustrations are excellent, leading to rapid identification down to family level.

BOOKS ON SPIDERS, ETC.

SAVORY, T. H. *The Spiders and Allied Orders of the British Isles.* Warne. Written for the beginner and contains useful information about other groups, such as mites, sea-spiders etc.

The Biology of Spiders. Sidgwick and Jackson. A good book on the biology of the world's spiders. Very readable and of value to the teacher who wishes to find among spiders examples of biological phenomena such as concealment, mimicry, instinct, symbiosis, predatory and parasitic habit etc.

Opiliones. Linnean Society of London. No. 1 in the series of "Synopses of the British Fauna." A formal description of the external characters of the group, but usable and complete. Ideal for the rarer species.

LOCKET, G. H. and MILLIDGE, A. F. *British Spiders.* Ray Society (1951–3). A compact book, usually easy to use with the aid of binocular and monocular microscopes. Requires a little practice. To be recommended as a first essential to those intending to study spiders seriously, or to identify a particular specimen.

INDEX